VAQUITA
Publishing

CW00530667

info @vaquitap±

07764 832077

Helen Seddon

Sender: Vaquita Publishing, PO Box 124, WELLINGTON, TA21 1BZ.

Why Have All The Animals Gone?

FROM: HELEN SEDDON
        RINGDOWN HOUSE
        GARLANDHAYES,
        CLAYHIDON
        CULLOMPTON
        DEVON EX15 3TT
        UNITED KINGDOM

Helen Seddon

ISBN: 978-1-9161705-0-6

Published by Vaquita Publishing

First published July 2019

Disclaimer

Every effort has been made to ensure that the information in this book is correct at the time of publication. The author and publisher do not assume and hereby disclaim any liability to any party for any loss, damage, or disruption caused by errors or omissions, whether such errors or omissions result from negligence, accident, or any other cause.

"We need another and a wiser and perhaps a more mystical concept of animals. Remote from universal nature, and living by complicated artifice, man in civilization surveys the creature through the glass of his knowledge and sees thereby a feather magnified and the whole image in distortion. We patronize them for their incompleteness, for their tragic fate of having taken form so far below ourselves. And therein we err, and greatly err. For the animal shall not be measured by man. In a world older and more complete than ours they move finished and complete, gifted with extensions of the senses we have lost or never attained, living by voices we shall never hear. They are not brethren, they are not underlings; they are other nations, caught with ourselves in the net of life and time, fellow prisoners of the splendour and travail of the earth."

Henry Beston

Contents

Author's Note

At the end of each chapter in this book, or in some cases sections within a chapter, there are details of charities and organisations that have been set up to help animals and wildlife on our planet. These organisations can provide you with further information, and explain about how you may help them, directly or indirectly. The more we know, the better we will understand and make a difference. These organisations, with your help and support, can be better placed to make an impact on our governments. They can help the governments to make a change; the sort of change that will not just stop species from becoming extinct, but ensure we forge a better future for everyone.

CHAPTER ONE
Are We Too Late To Put Things Right?

"The natural world is in serious trouble and it needs our help
as never before."

David Attenborough

The precipice of no return …

Let's not kid ourselves, we are on the precipice of no return. Our planet is in a weakened and desperate state. The time to act is NOW! For the last 25 years, we've been destroying our natural world at an unprecedented rate, with very little thought for the future. A UN scientific report released in May 2019, found that the devastation in our natural world is advancing at a rate that is hundreds of times faster than during the past 10 million years. It is estimated that more than one million species of animals and plants will be pushed into mass extinction during the next few decades. So, what are we doing about it? VERY LITTLE, is the answer. We are still hell-bent on destroying our planet's oceans, forests, rivers, soil, and even the air we breathe! If humanity were to stop and take a step back, we would see that we have made a terrible impact, by relentlessly damaging an estimated 75 per cent of land, and 40 per cent of the oceans on Earth. In doing so, we are not just destroying the natural world, but we are also harming ourselves.

Professor Robert Watson, an atmospheric chemist at the University of East Anglia, reminds us that, "We are eroding the very foundation of our economies, livelihoods, food security, health, and quality of life worldwide." We keep hearing that it's not too late to save our precious planet, but the economic differences between the world nations, as well as religious and political conflicts, mean that it is difficult to work together as a global unit. In fact, it almost seems an impossible task.

In the last 50 years alone, the human population has doubled. There are now nearly eight billion people living on our planet, and with modern technology and high living standards, human beings are living longer than ever before. Perhaps the biggest contributory factor to the devastation of our planet, is the speed at which we are growing our economies. What we call "improving our living standards" is in fact detrimental to the planet, and plays a key role in the devastation of wildlife and environment. In this period of 50 years (which is a mere fraction of the time that modern humans have been on the planet) we have wasted much of the world's unsustainable natural resources – fresh water, clean air, coal, oil, natural gas, phosphorus, other minerals, iron, soil, and timber. We have taken these resources without a thought for what will happen when they run out. Some resources, like oil, are non-renewable. Others, like drinking water, are becoming increasingly scarce as the population of humans continues to grow. The evidence is clear – this is not sustainable. But no matter how well informed we are, the consequences of our actions never appear to alarm us enough to make a sustained change. Already we are aware of climate change and the danger that this poses to our planet. From rapid deforestation to pollution of our seas and rivers, there can be no argument against protecting the planet's wildlife and environment. 2016 was an unstable year for our planet; it was also the hottest year on record. WWF's Living Planet Report declared that in just over 40 years, our world has seen a decline in wildlife of nearly 60% across land, sea, and freshwater. The report also acknowledges that by 2020 this will rise, with the estimated decline of two thirds of our wildlife. It's all the more shocking when you consider that this has happened in less than a generation. We should be very concerned about what is going on in the Arctic, because it is heating up at double the rate of the global average. Most of these extreme weather experiences are consistent with a changing climate. Scientists are telling us that 18 of the 19 warmest years since records began have taken place since the year 2001. Alas, the alarm bells are still not ringing loud enough for most people.

In the last 25 years alone, the human race has destroyed 10% of the planet's uninhabited and uncultivated areas – an area of destruction that measures twice the size of Alaska. Deforestation accounted for the loss of huge areas of primary forest in the Amazon, and a further 14% of primary forest in Central Africa. It's a twofold disaster. Not only are many species struggling to survive as a result of our aggressive action, but the carbon released into the atmosphere as a result of mass deforestation has rapidly accelerated the process of climate change. If current trends continue, then by the end of the century there will be no wild areas left. Dr James Watson of the University of Queensland and Wildlife Conservation Society states, "Without any policies to protect these areas [of wilderness], they are falling victim to widespread development. We probably have one to two decades to turn this around." Watson continues, "When you erode these wildernesses, they don't come back, you can't restore them. They will come back as something else, but you can't restore them."

This is our only planet. There isn't another planet that humans and wildlife can occupy when this one dies – no matter what fanciful stories we're told about Mars. We've got one shot, and we're blowing it.

Mother nature at its best

Human beings are often amazed at how nature is able to engineer its way back to where it should be. Natural regeneration can be defined as "the capability of an ecosystem to recover from devastation such as fire damage, or from human-caused processes acting upon the land." Before the damage, there is a healthy natural ecosystem in place. But, humans infringe on this, throwing things out of balance.

Possibly one of the best examples of natural regeneration in the world, was the reintroduction of wolves to Yellowstone Park in 1995. Located in northwest USA, Yellowstone was the world's first national park – extending over 3,500 square miles and protecting the wilderness for generations.

Back in the 1920s, the wolf was eradicated as a species in the park. Seventy years later, a small number of wolves were reintroduced after years of opposition (mainly from ranchers) on the grounds of potential loss of livestock. In 1974, a "wolf recovery team" was appointed. In 1982, the official recovery plan was put out for public comment. A second official recovery plan was released in 1985, followed by a poll for visitors to the park and more years of research and discussion. Eventually, an Enterprise Investment Scheme (EIS) was put out for public review in 1993. Two lawsuits filed in late 1994 threatened to jeopardise the recovery plan. One was by the Wyoming Farm Bureau, and the other by an affiliation of environmental groups – both lawsuits were thrown out. The adolescent wolves were captured in the Mackenzie Valley in Alberta, Canada and transported to Yellowstone Park. There was a last minute court order to stop the release of the wolves, provoked by the Wyoming Farm Bureau, but after 36 hours the wolves were judicially released into Yellowstone Park in 1995.

One of the main reasons for reintroducing the wolves was to reduce the elk population in the park. Despite efforts to control the elk, their numbers continued to increase, and they were reducing the vegetation in some areas to nothing. As predators, the wolves had a remarkable effect on the elk population – they changed the behaviour of the elk. The elk started to avoid certain areas of the park, like the valleys and the gorges where they would be more vulnerable to the wolves. These areas quickly started to regenerate. Within a few years, trees were growing taller, and species like aspen, cottonwood, and willow were returning.

The impact of reintroducing the wolves didn't just extend to plant life and elk, but other species too. The increased species of tree brought migratory birds, and beavers too – which by that point had almost disappeared from the park. Like the wolves, the beavers also supported the ecosystem by providing habitats for other animals, with their dams and eco-friendly structures on the rivers. Otters, muskrats, ducks, fish, reptiles, and amphibians all benefited from this. As the number of wolves increased, they started killing coyotes. In turn, this led to a rise in the number of rabbits and mice, who attracted more hawks, weasels, foxes, and badgers. The carrion the wolves left encouraged ravens and bald eagles to feast on the remains. Bears were attracted to the carrion and the berries from the regeneration of the trees. The bears also made an impact on the elk.

But what was even more incredible was that this trophic cascade of the ecological process – that started at the top of the food chain and dropped all the way down to the bottom – changed the rivers in the park. They meandered less, and there was less erosion. Some of the channels narrowed, and more pools formed, which was helpful for wildlife. The regeneration of the forests and vegetation meant that the rivers were more stabilised. Thanks to the elk moving out of the valleys, there was less soil erosion.

The reintroduction of the wolves was hailed as a great success, and opened up the minds of scientists as to the role that predators can play. While not everyone is convinced the wolves played such an important role, citing yearly weather changes as a decisive factor, it has opened up further areas for research in the future. Still though, the detractors remain. There are some who feel that the change in ecology and dynamics of Yellowstone since the reintroduction of the wolves, has been exaggerated. Furthermore, elk hunters have complained, claiming that the reduced number of elk has led to a major loss of revenue for the park, and that this is ultimately damaging to conservation. It's worth pointing out that said hunters didn't do a great job of controlling the elk prior to the reintroduction of wolves, and that these hunters seem to be impervious to the growing ecotourism industry. The tide is changing. People want to look at and photograph wildlife. They want to learn about wildlife and "see wildlife in the wild". The only shooting they want to do is with a video or camera. The majority of visitors to Yellowstone Park voted for the reintroduction of wolves, and it's believed that these visitors are boosting the local economy by millions of dollars every year. At the same time, they are helping to safeguard a large wilderness for hopefully many generations to come.

The Red List

The International Union for Conservation of Nature (IUCN) Red List is the most comprehensive record of the global conservation status of animal and plant species. The purpose of the Red List is to communicate the urgency and extent of conservation problems, to motivate the public and policy makers to reduce species extinction. Here are the definitions of the conservation status groups:

Conservation Status – IUCN Red List of Threatened Species

Extinct	(EX)	No known living individuals
Extinct in the wild	(EW)	Known only to survive in captivity, or as a naturalized population outside its historic range
Critically endangered	(CR)	Extremely high risk of extinction in the wild.
Endangered	(EN)	High risk of extinction in the wild.
Vulnerable	(VU)	Considered to be at high-risk of extinction, unless further action is taken.
Near threatened	(NT)	Likely to become endangered in the near future.
Least concern	(LC)	Lowest risk; does not qualify for a higher risk category.
Data deficient	(DD)	Not enough data to make an assessment of its risk of extinction.
Not evaluated	(NE)	Has not yet been evaluated against the criteria.

Throughout this book, I'll make constant reference to the Red List, as a way of demonstrating the plight of the species mentioned. Unfortunately, more often than not, our wild animals are near the top of the list.

Trophy hunting is not a sport … it's just wanton killing of wildlife!

Trophy hunting is defined as "the selective hunting of wild game for human recreation". The mere thought of humans hunting wildlife for amusement, as a leisure activity, or even for sport, will bring out strong opposing opinions. Opponents of trophy hunting feel it is immoral and sadistic, regardless of whether the animal killed is an endangered species. Many animals are not killed properly, and they have to suffer a long and agonising death. As one unrepentant trophy hunter stated in a newspaper article, "The elephant would be completely paralysed and not feeling any pain, but he's still breathing. Very large animals take a long time to die, there's no way round it." When questioned if it wouldn't have been better to aim for the elephant's head, he replied, "That's not my call." Perhaps the intention was never to shoot the elephant in the head, because the head is the trophy, which the hunter would want to place on the wall in his house. A bullet would have spoilt this. There appears to be no evidence, or very little at the most, that hunting brings in revenue for poor communities, or that it is of conservational benefit. Corrupt government officials in some countries are more likely to pocket the fees, and even prevent fees from going towards any conservation effort. The winners in this industry are the people who put on the trophy hunting safaris for wealthy tourists – tourists who pay anything from a few thousand dollars to hundreds of thousands of dollars. Every animal has a price on its head, regardless of whether it is an endangered species or not. At the end of the day, why would any normal and rational person book a holiday to shoot animals? Well, they do, and what's more they think it is right. But the one thing trophy hunters all have in common are the reasons they give to justify killing wildlife: 'It's good for conservation', 'There are more animals in the wild and it's natural for animals to be killed'. Some even quote the Bible and God's will to deliver the animals unto him. None of these reasons make sense, and there is no evidence behind their claims.

Trophy hunters want to kill the largest and most handsome specimens, and leave the smaller and weaker animals – which can impact the health and welfare of the species left to fend for themselves in the wild. For trophy hunters, it's all about the glory and excitement of killing the rarest animals. Social media is their platform to show off the animals they have killed. Photos are taken of the hunters proudly standing by or sitting on their prey, to show the world what they have done. All traces of blood are cleaned off the dead animal, and the carcass is then arranged neatly to show off its best features. The trophy is often the head of the animal, or the skin, and sometimes this includes other parts like paws and tails. In essence, anything that can be mounted on a wall to enhance the hunter's house when they bring their "trophy" home.

In the name of humanity, stop killing elephants and rhinos

An insatiable desire for ivory products in Asia has led to the slaughter of tens of thousands of elephants in Africa. The number of elephants has dropped by 62% over the last 10 years, and the future of elephants in the wild is grim. They could be verging on extinction by the end of the next decade. Even Asian elephants are classified as an endangered species, with less than 40,000 in the wild across 13 Asian countries. This is mainly due to the serious shrinking of their natural habitat, as they are trying to survive in the most densely populated areas in the world.

The statistics make even more dire reading for rhinos. In Africa, large scale poaching has driven some rhino populations to extinction. Some numbers have risen, largely thanks to breeding programmes and reintroduction of rhinos into areas they once populated, all aided by the persistent efforts of conservation organisations and armed protection units. However, the future is still tenuous for the African rhino, due to the rhino horn trade in Southeast Asia. In Asia, the rhino population is similarly critically endangered, where two Javan subspecies have become extinct and the third subspecies has as few as 35 animals left in a single park.

Both elephants and rhinos are keystone species. They play an important role in balancing natural ecosystems, and their natural environment could be drastically affected without them. In particular, they are essential for conserving the savanna grasslands. By pulling down trees and trampling scrub areas, they create grassland, making areas for smaller species to co-exist. Forest elephants push down trees and bushes to bring light into the forests for plants to grow, allowing smaller animals to live in the forest. Rhinos and elephants also have an important role in scattering seeds. Both have extremely slow digestion, meaning that as seeds pass their way through the animal's body, they are dispersed over a wide area – via their dung – as they move through the forests and grasslands. This makes rhinos and elephants vital to forest regeneration.

Wake up to the plight of big cats in the wild

Looking at the number of big cats surviving in the wild, these species are in so much trouble. The tiger has managed to buck the trend, and in 2017 there were an estimated 3,890 tigers in the wild, mostly in Asia. Something to celebrate, you might think. But when you consider that there are an estimated 5,000-7,000 tigers in captivity in the USA, with little to no regulation on their welfare, then we should be appalled. There must be many more thousands of tigers in countries across the world, but we have no idea of statistics. They are also likely to be hybrid, meaning they have been crossed with a different subspecies of tiger or crossed with lions and leopards. Ownership and breeding are not monitored, with many of them kept in backyards, city apartments, and breeding farms. The illegal trade in tiger products is fuelled by the black market on captive tigers, which then stimulates demand for tiger poaching in the wild.

A century ago, there were an estimated 200,000 wild lions in Africa. Today, there are an estimated 20,000 left in the wild. The species is now classified as critically endangered, and lions are now extinct in 26 African countries.

South Africa has the largest number of lion farms, and the plight of lions in these farms is absolutely dreadful – because they have been bred for the bullet. Many other species of wild cat, like leopards, cheetahs, and jaguars, to name a few, are also suffering catastrophic decline in numbers, and their future is very insecure.

If we help save dolphins and whales, we are saving ourselves

Whether in the wild or in captivity, the dolphins and whales on our planet are continually threatened by human action. Indirect human action can be as ordinary as tens of thousands of dolphins dying every year, because they have got caught up in fishing nets and drowned. Direct human action involves the slaughter of dolphins and whales, for food, tradition, research, or sport. Taiji in Japan hosts the notorious "dolphin slaughters" for six months of the year, driving dolphins and small whales into the cove from their migratory paths. Several thousand are slaughtered each year, despite intense criticism and horror from across the world at the cruel and barbaric methods used to kill them.

Similarly, around 1,000 pilot whales are slaughtered each summer in the Faroe Isles. The Faroese jump into the water to meet the whales, who have been deliberately driven inland. This is known as the "Grindadrap", or "Grind" for short. The locals take their spinal lances and stab the whales, with the sea turning red from the blood. The Faroese defend the killings, calling the Grindadrap "a tradition" – the hunt is legal and the pilot whale is not an endangered species. Both the slaughters in Taiji and the Faroe Islands provide meat for human consumption, but thanks to the pollution of the seas this meat is toxic, with high levels of mercury. This is confirmed by both Japanese and the Faroese medical experts, who recommend that people don't eat it, because it isn't safe for consumption.

This, of course, brings us to pollution – which is directly down to human activity. We have been polluting the oceans on such a scale that the high acidity rate is killing our coral reefs and small marine animals with shells. It has been estimated that as much as a quarter of all man-made emissions are absorbed by the sea, which leads to acidification. Most of our trash that enters the sea is plastic. Then there is oil from boats, airplanes, cars, and trucks, and let's not forget the chemical discharges. These come from raw sewage, factories, and agriculture fertilisers to name a few. So, dolphins and whales have a lot to contend with in our oceans – and when they become contaminated it will ultimately kill them. If that doesn't finish them off, then we have Japan, Iceland, and Norway out on the high seas, killing large whales in the most brutal fashion – in blatant disregard of the International Whaling Commission (IWC), which has placed a ban on killing whales for 89 member countries across the world.

Keep animals in the wild – where they belong

We've all been to the zoo or the circus, and gaped at wild animals in their enclosures, cages, and aquariums. But how can this equate with the space these animals have in the wild? Even safari parks can't always provide adequate room for lions, tigers, elephants, giraffes, zebras, rhinos, and so on. Animals that have been born in captivity still have the genes of an animal born in the wild. Wild animals in captivity can suffer in different ways. They can be fed a reasonable diet, kept in clean surroundings, able to exercise, and have company, but they will still suffer from the typical signs of mental distress brought on by captivity. Many of us will have seen the pacing polar bear, the swaying elephant, or the small monkey hiding in the corner. The other end of the spectrum is dire, where animals are kept in filthy, cramped enclosures, with a poor diet and no company. They die early – from disease, depression, and hunger. Then there are animals forced to perform in circuses, living in small containers, travelling on the road to different venues for months on end. There are some zoos and circuses across the world where they don't need to adhere to basic regulations, because there are no animal welfare laws in place to enforce these.

There are many animals that don't fare well in captivity, and dolphins and whales are at the top of the list. Their natural home is in the vast oceans, living in family pods and enjoying thousands of miles of freedom. How can anyone compare that with tanks in marine parks and dolphinariums? Highly intelligent creatures, forced to eat dead fish and live in chlorinated water; forced to perform tricks in front of audiences day after day; swimming in endless circles, becoming depressed and stressed with boredom – their life span is drastically shortened in captivity through illness, confinement, and a lack of social stimuli. How can this be called entertainment? In reality, it will only end when humans stop buying tickets to see animals in captivity.

Look beyond the pageantry of hunting with foxhounds

The UK Hunting Ban was passed in 2004, and the ban on hunting with dogs in the UK became law in February 2005. The law covered the hunting of foxes, deer, hares, and mink, and was based on the premise that hunting is a cruel and unnecessary "sport". Some forms of hunting were exempt from the ban, but still constrained to limits on how many dogs could be used. Prior to the ban, organised hunts used packs of hounds. After the ban, the hunts devised something called "trail hunting", which was broadly based on drag hunting. In drag hunting, an artificial scent is laid by a human runner over several specified lines or routes with jumps and obstacles. The hounds follow the scent, with a field of mounted riders in pursuit. Drag hunting does not involve the hunting of live animals. Organised hunts with packs of foxhounds lay a trail of fox scent for the hounds, and mounted riders chase after the hounds. The problem is that the hounds frequently but "accidentally" pick up the scent of a live fox, and then chase and kill the fox. There has also been enough video evidence of fox hunts taking place up and down the country, without laying any trail scent. In other words – hunting is pretty much the same as before the ban, with the help of terriermen blocking badger setts and digging out foxes when they go to ground. There is also video evidence of "cub hunting", which entails allowing fox cubs to be attacked and eaten by young hounds, so that the dogs get a taste for killing foxes. Meanwhile, the hunts continue to claim that hunting is "a British tradition", and therefore should not be banned. While there is evidence that hunting is not as popular as it has been in the past, with some hunts giving up the practice altogether, and others amalgamating with neighbouring hunts, the hunting ban still needs to be tightened. There are too many loopholes and differing interpretations which have helped the hunts to avoid prosecution for killing wildlife. Stag hunters blatantly hunt and chase stags to exhaustion, which is illegal. There have been many witness accounts where the huntsmen have behaved despicably, lying and even threatening people. One woman was told that the hunt would set their hounds on her, when she interfered by not allowing the hunters into her garden – where a stag had sought refuge. Hunt monitors and saboteurs have suffered serious injuries at the hands of terriermen, or have been knocked over by riders on horses. Their vehicles have been rammed and damaged by terriermen and hunt supporters. It's a war out there, and hunters are hell-bent on breaking the law because they want to pursue and kill our wildlife.

Why are badgers subject to such gruesome wildlife crime in the UK?

Badger baiting really highlights the barbaric brutality of wildlife crime that is happening in our countryside. This barbaric practice involves torturing badgers to death, and appears to be a thriving "sport" across the UK. Terriers are sent down badger setts to locate the badgers, so the baiters can dig them out. They are then set upon by dogs, where the badger bravely fights back, even if the baiters have "disabled" the creature in some way to lessen the injuries to the dogs. Badgers and their setts are protected by the *1992 Badger Act*, and baiters can receive a hefty fine and a prison sentence. But, it doesn't appear to deter them from killing badgers.

Between 2013 and 2018, nearly 70,000 badgers were culled. In the 2018 badger cull, 32,601 badgers were shot or trapped, with bounties of £50 being placed on each badger's head. In the original culling trials in 2013, the Independent Expert Panel (IEP) were not impressed with the way badgers were being shot. They expressed an opinion that the overall standard of competence amongst the contractors needed to be raised for future badger culls. The Department for Environment, Food & Rural Affairs (DEFRA) did not invite the IEP to monitor any more culls – judging that it wasn't necessary to monitor and ensure that badgers were killed humanely. There was some kickback against this verdict, and the Badger Trust took the issue to court, asserting that an IEP was necessary for the protection and welfare of badgers. Unfortunately, their case was ultimately dismissed. Later in this book, I'll discuss this particular situation in more depth.

Humans are responsible for pollution in the oceans

We are all responsible for the pollution in our oceans. We are people: small businesses, large businesses, governments, global businesses, oil companies, shipping companies, villages, towns, and farms. The main causes of ocean pollution are industrial waste, agricultural waste, sewage, toxic chemicals, nuclear waste, plastic waste, acid rain, and oil spillages. Millions of tons of plastic end up in the oceans every year. And it's all put there by people. Plastic pollution has a catastrophic effect on wildlife. Whales, dolphins, seals, turtles, sea birds, and fish can consume plastic or get entangled. They die from suffocation, starvation, and drowning. Plastic waste is responsible for killing up to one million sea birds a year.

Every one of us uses and disposes plastic. Every one of us has to cut down on plastic, and recycle responsibly. We can all do something to reduce the amount of plastic finding its way into the sea. Start by reducing the use of single-use plastics like disposable cutlery, straws, plastic bags, and containers. Recycle all plastic. Don't use products containing microbeads. Join groups that organise beach or river clean ups. Look for ways of reducing plastic in your everyday life, and spread the word about plastic pollution. Reduce your use of plastic – do it for our marine wildlife. We cannot let them suffer and die because of our irresponsibility.

Poached, hunted, deforested, and eaten to extinction

Saving endangered wildlife is more important now than ever before. Humanity has only itself to blame. Everything in the natural world is connected. Every time a species of animal or plant becomes extinct, it upsets the balance of nature, thereby changing the ecosystem. We can no longer sustain the killing of wildlife for trophies. We can no longer take wildlife habitats for human needs – too much has been taken already. We must stop killing animals for ivory, horns, scales, skin, bones, teeth, paws, and every other body part imaginable – there is no scientific evidence that these things can help or cure medical problems. The only thing we achieve by doing this, is to accelerate the decline of animals in the wild, pushing them ever closer to extinction. Shop ethically, and do not buy items made from endangered animals. Be an ethical tourist, and do not exploit animals under any circumstances during holidays. Commit to learning about the risks to wildlife, and reduce your carbon footprint.

A few last words ...

Empowering people, families, and individuals to get involved is a good experience. We all want to know that we can make a difference, and in turn this makes us feel good about ourselves. The truth is, we can all choose to be involved by committing to even small changes in our daily lives to help the planet. Be a voice for wildlife. We share this planet, and we do not have a moral right to assume that animals exist for us and that we can treat them as we like. They have the same right to live on this earth as we do.

CHAPTER TWO
Trophy Hunting

"The greatness of a nation and its moral progress can be judged by the way its animals are treated. I hold that the more helpless a creature the more entitled it is to protection by man from the cruelty of humankind."

Mahatma Gandhi

What is trophy hunting?

Trophy hunting can be described as "the shooting of selected animals for pleasure and recreation". Hunters often set their sights on big game species like rhinos, elephants, lions, pumas, and bears, but ultimately it all depends on the hunter's budget. Most hunters have to rely on many less alluring and more affordable species to hone their skills and satisfy their craving for killing wild animals. Going after the larger species is usually a lifelong ambition, and can easily cost many hundreds of thousands of dollars. A suitable rifle for big game hunting can set a hunter back up to $200,000, and a fourteen-day African safari hunt can cost up to $80,000. It's estimated that, every year, tens of thousands of different species of wild animals are killed by American trophy hunters at home, and in foreign countries across the world. Many of these species are endangered or on the critical list. Yet some foreign governments allow this practice, refusing to illegalise it.

The majority of people cannot sympathise with anyone who pays tens of thousands of dollars to kill an innocent creature for pleasure and trophies. The trophy is the head of the animal, the skin, or other body parts. Sometimes, it's the whole animal, which is kept as a "souvenir" to take home and put on display. After the kill, the animal carcass is carefully arranged for the trophy hunter to kneel or stand next to it with their weapon, and pose for a photograph. Bloody wounds are carefully hidden, so the animal is perceived to be sleeping calmly or at peace with nature.

There is usually very little skill involved in this – everything is organised for the trophy hunters. They are taken to the animal and even told where to stand and when to shoot. Many shoot incompetently, even at close range, leaving the animal to die in agony. For the price they pay, all trophy hunters expect a successful hunt, and everything is taken care of to achieve the outcome of sending them home with their chosen trophy.

Trophy hunters like to display their trophies in their office or in specially designed trophy rooms back in their homes. They may call them "game rooms" or "gun rooms", and sometimes they put the weaponry they have used to kill their victims on display in the same room. The number of dead animal trophies is a sign of the trophy hunter's social status. It's a way of boasting to their friends and colleagues about how much they can afford to lavish on their recreational pastime. Acquiring trophy animals is also the trophy hunter's way of displaying power. Trophy rooms can allow trophy hunters to relive their adventures amongst the body parts and stuffed carcasses of dead animals they have slaughtered. Some might describe this as a way of documenting their butchery of wildlife over the years. The dead animal heads on show have a macabre and ghoulish look about them. Most people have a total lack of understanding as to why any human would want to kill such precious wildlife, or why anyone would want to sit amongst taxidermic formations in a room within their home. But then, if you find pleasure in being a sadistic serial animal killer, then this behaviour could be called appropriate.

Depending on their budget, trophy hunters also pay hunt outfitters to find the best deals on the animals they want to kill for their collection. These guys know the market, and can help their clients with everything from flights, accommodation, legally transporting firearms, and the ins and outs of CITES and other custom checks, so they can be confident of clearing their trophies and getting them home. The trophy hunters pay for the services of experienced, knowledgeable guides, whose expertise will provide them with the best chance of a successful hunt. Once they bag their chosen trophy animals, they have to pay the trophy fee for each animal killed. Obviously, the trophy hunter will have been informed of the price in advance. In Africa, if they have reached their goal of hunting and killing all of the "Big 5" (rhino, elephant, lion, leopard, and buffalo) on their "safari" before it comes to an end, they can always use their remaining time to kill more common prey. But that will be one expensive expedition, and out of reach for many trophy hunters these days.

When it comes to the actual killing, you will not be surprised to learn that trophy hunters rely on some particularly unsavoury and cruel methods. There's no fair-chase hunting, where the prey has a reasonable chance of escaping. Getting away alive does not come into the trophy tradition. Baiting often includes leaving large amounts of food for wild animals. The animals eagerly come forward to devour the bait, making them easy targets for trophy hunters waiting in a concealed spot. Usually, this bait contains substances to drug the animals, giving the trophy hunter an easier kill. Hunting with a pack of hounds, who wear radio-collars, to pursue targeted trophy animals is another cruel practice. The frightened prey animals are pursued until exhausted, where they might seek refuge in a tree or risk fighting the hounds on the ground in order to escape. If they choose the former, they will be shot down from the tree, as the hounds bay for their blood. If they choose the latter, it goes without saying that one exhausted animal has no chance against a pack of hounds and a trophy hunter with a rifle, standing a few feet away. Inevitably, young animals are killed or left orphaned when adults are rousted out of hiding by a pack of hounds, and then unfairly slain to become a souvenir.

Another horrific method used by trophy hunters, is the setting of traps or snares for targeted wildlife. This has to be the most inhumane and cowardly way of catching and killing trophy animals. Animals can languish for hours and even days in these traps, whilst suffering from broken limbs and various ghastly injuries, not to mention starvation and dehydration. But it is an easy kill for the trophy hunter, who only has to walk up to the frightened and injured creature and shoot it from a few feet away. The traps and snares don't always catch the coveted trophy quarry. Often, other wildlife animals of no interest to trophy hunters are trapped and sometimes pets have met their fate in a snare too. It is probably fair to say that not all trophy hunters are accomplished in the art of tracking, stalking, and killing wildlife, which makes these activities totally abhorrent and cruel.

There are a host of technical gadgets and equipment on hand for trophy hunters these days, from high powered guns to precision-guided rifles, pistols with limited kickback to bows with fantastic speed; the level of weapon accuracy can be over three times what it was just ten years ago. Aerial drones are handy, sending videos and images to trophy hunters' phones. These drones don't fall under the *Federal Airborne Hunting Act 1972*, which prohibits tracking, harassing, and shooting animals via manned aircraft. Two-way radio headsets, heat sensors, motion detectors, infrared lighting, high powered telescopes, and armour-piercing bullets are just a few of the many items on offer to help trophy hunters bag their trophies. This is the grim reality of trophy hunting in the early twenty-first century.

While trophy hunting has staunch supporters, who feel that hunting and killing animals is a gratifying sport, there is very little to acquaint it with the meaning of "sport". The trophy hunter does not compete on a level playing field with the prey. The trophy hunter may profess to enjoy his endeavours in slaughtering wildlife, but then the odds are stacked in his favour. Meanwhile, his "opponent" is doing nothing more than fleeing for their life. The trophy hunter doesn't hunt for food, to protect livestock, or cull to reduce the size of a species. They want the "prize" – which is the animal with the biggest antlers, tusks, or horns. They want to take the best and biggest animals as trophies, leaving behind a decimated gene pool for the future. This is catastrophic for wildlife, because it's leading to inevitable extinction of many species. Let's be clear that trophy hunting is not a sport, but more akin to a violent and cruel orgy of senseless killing for fun and pleasure.

While trophy hunting has long been a booming business across Africa, its future is beginning to look precarious. Years of corruption, encouraging hunters and guides to break the law to kill endangered species, are taking a toll. Trophy hunting has also been a cover for wildlife crime and poaching. Interestingly, the hunt outfitters are beginning to see the future, and it's not looking good for them. As one safari company says in its literature: "Hunting the Big 5 in Africa is a dream trip for many hunters, but the opportunity window may be closing." Waning public support for hunting in general, and especially those animals considered endangered, has led to a flurry of new legal restrictions and even hunting bans in some countries. Finally, countries are seeing the alternative source of revenue from ecotourism as having a far more beneficial impact. The revenue derived from ecotourism dwarfs the amount derived from trophy hunting. It makes a mockery of the claim by the hunting fraternity that trophy hunting has a huge, positive impact on local people and conservation in Africa.

As time goes by, and the world wises up to the crimes of trophy hunters, opportunities for senseless trophy hunting are declining rapidly. People are beginning to recognise that hunting is a barbaric activity, which has a negative impact upon the country in which it takes place. For some endangered species, there is still hope. The question is, will time be on their side?

Safari Club International (SCI)

This is the organisation that fuels trophy hunters' lust and ambition for killing and collecting animal trophies. Founded in 1971, and based in Tucson, Arizona, SCI holds an annual convention attracting thousands of trophy hunters, and is well known for its auctions for the right to kill various animals including endangered species. It's an organisation dedicated to preserving hunters' rights, and at the same time "promoting wildlife conservation". SCI claims to have 170 groups or "chapters" globally, with 80 of them in the USA and nearly 50,000 members worldwide. They see themselves as a "political force" in Washington and other capital cities around the world to further their members' hunting activities. They say this has been achieved by forging partnerships with "like-minded" organisations, and by spending millions of dollars each year "to protect the freedom to hunt through policy advocacy, litigation and education for federal and state legislators to ensure hunting is protected for future generations." More recently, they have stated that they want their members to promote a good image of hunting to non-hunters through their words and actions. Obviously, this is in response to growing adverse reaction from all over the world to the wanton killing of wildlife. A good example was the dishonourable and unethical killing of Cecil the lion in Zimbabwe. Cecil's killer was immediately suspended as a member of SCI amidst the backlash from people around the world. After the Zimbabwe authorities only brought charges against the killer's guide, the killer himself was quickly reinstated as a member of SCI.

While practising "ethical hunting" in the field, members are also encouraged to support humanitarian efforts across the globe through SCI's own charity – Safari Club International Foundation. The SCI Foundation's mission statement is very broad and simple: "The SCI Foundation funds and directs worldwide programs dedicated to wildlife conservation and outdoor education". That word conservation, which also appears to be dominant on websites of other hunting groups across the globe, comes up frequently on SCI's website. They claim to be passionate about wildlife, ecosystem management, sustainability, preserving and managing natural resources, and helping to provide quality habitats for all species – whilst still being hunters and taking pride in their rich hunting heritage.

SCI's charitable work appears to be steeped in education, and what better place to start than with high school students? When young minds are introduced to the SCI organisation, they take part in team building exercises, along with talks on conservation and ecology. Then, they are ready to learn outdoor skills, such as shooting, fly fishing, and archery, with some hiking and camping – all the things you need to learn to start hunting. They offer a number of grants and scholarships to young people on education programmes, and are keen to attract more female students. It's all about investing in the members of the future. Their "humanitarian services" cover their individual members, who have overcome their challenges in life and are helped to continue their outdoor activities. They also give their time to promote hunting for disabled people, and they are happy to help blind people hunt too. They believe in reaching out to the disabled – who are "really in a 'dark' place when they find them" – and giving these people hope for the future. Many of these people are unemployable and severely depressed, but once they start hunting with the SCI Foundation the transformation is incredible. Apparently they smile uncontrollably once they are given a fly rod or a shotgun. The quality of their lives improves when they discover "the freedom in the hunt".

One event in the calendar that must not be missed is the Annual SCI Convention, which now also incorporates SCI's Foundation Day. This is a huge convention that goes on for a period of four days, with traders selling all the hunting equipment that you could possibly imagine. What better way to encourage more people to hunt? With hunt outfitters at the ready to organise that big hunting trip, firearms experts to help you find that rifle or gun that you feel comfortable with, professional hunters offering a guarantee to take you to that specific trophy animal you want to bag, clothing experts at your service to help you look the part out in the field, taxidermists to give you the download on how to get your trophy on the wall, and all the razzmatazz that goes with spending big bucks – it's truly a hunter's paradise. There are auctions for the rights to kill every animal that can be hunted in the world, and prices range from hundreds of dollars to hundreds of thousands of dollars for one of the big five endangered species on the African continent. Sign up for membership and get SCI's bi-monthly glossy magazine full of adverts for trophy hunting. It's all about the modern hunter having the means to express him or herself as a glorious upstanding member of the human race, and a saviour to all animals worth killing.

In order to further encourage their members to hunt, SCI holds competitions where trophy hunters who lack any competent skills can compete with the more experienced and professional hunters. SCI has *The Official Record Book of Trophy Animals*, which immortalises the achievements of winners in 29 categories and hundreds of subcategories. In order to win all the categories, one trophy hunter would need to kill 322 animals of different species or subspecies from around the world. Each category is based on a species. For example, there is the "Bears of the World Grand Slam". To win this, a trophy hunter would have to bag an Alaskan brown bear, a Eurasian brown bear, a grizzly, and a polar bear. That's a lot of money in trophy fees. The "African Big Five Grand Slam" would require a trophy hunter with even deeper pockets to bag a buffalo, a rhinoceros, an elephant, a lion, and a leopard. Then there are more honours within each grand slam category, based on tusk length, antler size, horn size, weight of the animal, etc. All in the name of conservation, of course …

What is ranch hunting?

Ranch hunting is held on ranches or private estates where animals are specifically bred in captivity or brought in for the purpose of trophy hunting. These ranches and estates can be found in countries all over the world, and that includes the UK; from Russia to Argentina, Canada to Mexico, Europe to the USA, New Zealand, Australia, and so on. The state of Texas in the USA has over 500 ranches alone. It is big business, and a big draw for trophy hunters. Exotic game come at a high price, especially if they are rare in the wild. Take the bongo antelope, for example. A typical trophy fee for this animal is $35,000. The ranches which own bongo antelope claim that it has an estimated world population of 700. Interestingly, the Kenyan conservation group Mt Kenya Wildlife Conservancy, are quoting the bongo antelope as "near threatened" by extinction. They have in their care, living as semi-wild, seventy two bongos with four calves born in 2017. In 2018, they estimate there were less than 250 mature individual bongos in the wild, which is the threshold required to make up a genetically stable population. A viable option to restock the forests would be to bring in some of the 750 bongos living in zoos and parks across the world. There are also some 200 bongos on ranches in the USA, which could be translocated to Kenya. But with the high price of a bongo trophy, and a wildly overestimated number of bongos in the wild given out by ranches to conciliate conservation opinion, it doesn't bode well. It seems unlikely that a business whose income relies on the slaughter of exotic species for trophies would be interested in giving up their bongo stock animals, to live back on their native land.

Another game animal, the American bison, has a current trophy fee of $6,500, with a quoted estimated world population of 500,000 by relevant ranches on their website. Needless to say, this figure isn't what it seems. Yes, there are approximately 500,000 bison living across America, but we need to understand the background. Originally there were between 20 to 30 million roaming the North American landscape. But due to habitat loss and unregulated shooting by hunters, the population was reduced to 1,091 in 1889. So, how come there are half a million bison today? In order to increase the numbers, they were cross-bred with cattle being raised on ranches as livestock. Today, fewer than 30,000 purebred bison are in conservation herds, and fewer than 5,000 are roaming "unfenced and disease-free". So, what are these ranches offering? It would be a travesty if they had purebred American bison for trophy hunting.

In the UK, paid hunts on estates offer "deer stalking", with a range of different deer species available. This comes under the category of field sports, which are legal on private land. Yet there have been reports of mountain goats in North Wales being offered for up to £1,000 a kill. These goats are not a domestic breed which has escaped, but are a wild species that have been roaming Snowdonia for 10,000 years. The authorities are happy to cull them, so that there is more grazing for sheep, to protect young trees, and to help avoid vehicle accidents. Residents have complained about the goats getting into their gardens and generally being a nuisance. It appears to be a sad situation when you have a wildlife species that has been living in this area since the last ice age, only for them to be seen as a problem which should go away. Putting a few of them in a zoo is not a solution, and the government should be seeking more creative means for dealing with the wild mountain goat species in Wales.

The absurd reality is that the majority of trophy hunters are actually hunting captive animals on these private ranches and estates. To help them further, ranches can offer high fence hunting, which is a form of "canned hunting". Again, this is not a fair-chase situation, and it's easy to bag trophies for the trophy hunters – who have no hunting skills and are pushed for time. When confining herds of deer within a high fenced area, there has been overcrowding, with the outbreak of some chronic and wasting diseases amongst such herds. But then the argument the ranchers use in defence is that more and more land is being sold to developers, and therefore there is less natural habitat for these animals. Many of the exotic animals actually come from unlicensed roadside zoos in the USA, though the larger zoos will sell off older or surplus animals they have bred. When travelling between destinations, it has been established that some zoo animals (like lions and tigers) which are kept in cages for their entire life, are shot by trophy hunters as soon as they are let out of their transport caging. Their only value was being a trophy with a price on their head. Many trophy hunters prefer killing zoo animals, as they are easier targets – being used to people – and are usually in better condition than those from the wild. Hence, they make better looking trophies to display on the wall back home.

In the past, a publication named *The Animal Finder's Guide* (AFG) would send out regular newsletters regarding the trade in exotic animals. It was originally started to help people who were keeping and raising exotic species. Hunting ranch owners used the guide, posting adverts for sales and auctions. *The Finder's Guide* would get all sorts of exotic animals on request from private owners, zoos, and remote places abroad. The animals would then be found, trapped, caged, and transported across North America and some other countries, only to end up on hunt ranches to be shot by trophy hunters.

Although the AFG is no longer in existence, animal auctions continue. Some animals are bred on the ranches, but they too will end up being cornered and shot. Dealing in exotic animals is a very sad business and appears to have no links with conservation. It seems that the AFG themselves gave up on the notion of supporting species in the wild. In a statement, they said, "Since the world is losing natural habitat daily, it is our belief that the last hope before extinction for many animal species is captive breeding." Captive breeding is a lucrative business, with the animals bred being sold for profit. Every year, tens of thousands of these animals are slaughtered by trophy hunters on ranches, in the USA and in other countries. There's no thought, care, or connection to where said animals originated from, or where their ancestors once lived in the wild. There's no conservation effort that's worth a mention here. Breeding wild animals on such a scale in captivity, is not a replacement for keeping species safe in their natural habitat. These animals are the products of commercial enterprises – whose sole concern is making money, regardless of where these animals end up after they are sold. To contemplate this morally indefensible situation is difficult. It is a particularly dark and harrowing affair.

What is canned hunting?

Canned hunting is an extreme form of trophy hunting, where animals, mainly lions, are bred in captivity on ranches in South Africa for hunters to shoot them in confined areas. It goes without saying that this is inexcusable, unforgiveable, brutal, and barbaric. Canned hunting also takes place on hunt ranches in North America, but nothing is comparable to what goes on at some of the ranches in South Africa. Lions are bred in deplorable conditions. Hunting in Africa is expensive, and it takes time – days or weeks – to find prey. So, business-minded people have found an opportunity to speed things up by breeding trophy animals on farms. Hunters can now come out to South Africa from anywhere in the world, kill a lion, and go back home within a couple of days. They know they will make a killing, because the animals are taken from the compound and let loose in a restricted area where their death is guaranteed.

Farming these lions is completely unethical, and against the animal's welfare. It is not illegal, however, and the lion farmers know that. They generally do as little as humanly possible for these animals in regards to nutrition and veterinary care. The lions are reared for the sole purpose of being shot by trophy hunters. There are around two hundred farms breeding lions, and estimated figures show there are about 8,000 captive lions for canned hunting. In the wild, South Africa has an estimated 2-3,000 lions.

From birth to death

Born in captivity, the cubs are taken away from the lioness within a few hours of being born, and are bottle fed for 8 weeks. Taking them away so young means they miss out on the essential colostrum of first milk, thereby giving the cub a deficient start in life and causing health problems early on. They are taken away straight after birth, for two reasons. Firstly, as young cubs they will be fed and handled by humans, making them suitable to be used in petting zoos. The second reason for taking away the cubs at birth, is that this means the lioness will quickly come in season again. Thus, the lioness can have as many as five litters every two years. In the wild, lionesses will take care of their cubs, who are weaned at six months from their mother's milk. The cubs will continue to stay with their mother until they are two to three years old. But on the canned farm it's a never ending production line of lion cubs.

Tourists who visit these petting zoos or farms are usually unaware of the future for these young cubs. They are paying for the experience of being close to and being able to touch what they see as exotic wildlife – a once in a lifetime experience. They are lured in, believing they are visiting a wildlife sanctuary, fed lies that they are helping to save the species. These farms also take on young volunteers from countries around the world, who also believe they are helping with conservation and preserving the lion species. Behind the façade of the petting zoos and farms is a repellent and horrific industry.

When they are no longer suitable for the petting zoo, the cubs are then transferred to a caged compound – a miserable, lethargic life where they are bored and underfed. Some lions will mate and some will fight each other. They will end their life of around 4 to 7 years, by being shot by a trophy hunter. They may be taken off the farm to be hunted and shot elsewhere. When they are transferred to a new place, they wander around listlessly, not knowing what to do on their own. They cannot escape from the "can" or enclosure. Sometimes they are fed bait, and sometimes that bait may contain drugs to sedate the lion. When they see the vehicle transporting the trophy hunter, they can be encouraged to come nearer to the vehicle to be shot. A whistle can get the lion's attention just before the bullet is fired. The weapon used to shoot them can be a rifle, a handgun, or a crossbow. The trophy hunter will shoot the lion from the safety of the back of the vehicle, at close range. It's all completely legal in South Africa. Trophy hunters don't need a licence, and they don't require any hunting skills. Anyone can go and hunt lions in South Africa, which means many canned lions are not killed with the first shot. The statistic is even higher when the trophy hunters use the bow and arrow option. The lions are then left to endure an agonising death. Born and bred for the gun, they are doomed to suffer throughout their short lives, to be rewarded with nothing less than an excruciating painful end. The exorbitant price a majestic animal pays, to end up on the wall as a trophy, somewhere on the other side of the world.

Trophy hunters will pay up to $50,000 to shoot a lion in a canned hunt. It's a multi-million dollar industry in South Africa, fuelled by the number of wealthy individuals from around the world who want to kill a trophy lion with minimum amount of effort and time. Fifty per cent of the trophy hunters come from the USA. They can go on the web and actually choose their trophy lion in the comfort of their home. The price for each lion is given, with the males being the more expensive. At the top end will be white male lions, and male lions with black manes. At the other end of the scale will be lionesses and even cubs who have been offered by some ranches. In a single year, about 1,000 lions are slain this way. It's all about money, and whilst trophy hunters are prepared to throw thousands and thousands of dollars at this industry, the cruelty and barbarity will continue – not just for lions, but for other species too, including tigers, springbok, and crocodiles. Another sordid practice that canned farms have begun, is legally sending lion carcasses to Southeast Asia, where the bones and body parts are used in traditional medicine. The South African government has passed laws allowing up to 800 carcasses for export. The canned farms have welcomed this profitable export outlet, which allows them to make even more money from the lions. Unfortunately, this can only encourage the trade of exporting lion bones to Asia, and consequently increases the benefits for poachers in the wild. Now is the time for South Africa to deal with unethical canned hunting and the export of lion bones. South Africa was once a country that was proud of its ethical tourism, a country of stunning wildlife and nature. Instead, it is now a country where 200 farms breed lions for the bullet. What happened to the vision of the lion as the majestic king of all beasts? Where other African countries are looking to ecotourism and the benefits it can bring to the long term future, South Africa continues to endorse the soulless slaughter of innocent creatures. Instead of leading the way forward, South Africa is living in the past.

"Blood Lions"

The documentary film "Blood Lions" exposed South Africa's controversial canned lion hunting industry to the world. The film has been viewed in 185 countries, at numerous film festivals, in parliaments and special interest groups, and at every major tourist conference in Europe and Africa. "Blood Lions" has opened the eyes and minds of many people, as well as the tourism industry, who are now better informed about the links between lion cub petting and canned hunting. The Professional Hunters Association of South Africa has also come out and stated that canned hunting practices are no longer defendable. It's not just about the barbaric nature of the practice either. People are recognising that canned hunting has not helped the conservation of lions in the wild, because of the confusing and misleading messages it has sent out about justifying the exploitation of lions for profit. It has confused conservation challenges and priorities. On the contrary, it has actually encouraged the poaching of wild lions, because these canned farms need a constant supply of new blood in their breeding programmes. Furthermore, these captive lions can never be released back into the wild. They are "genetically contaminated", not afraid of humans, and therefore dangerous. They are also not likely to survive by hunting for their own food.

The effect of trophy hunting on wildlife and conservation

A common theme amongst trophy hunters is that they believe what they do is valuable to controlling wildlife populations. But this doesn't make any sense, especially when hunt ranchers are breeding wild animals year after year to sell and kill them. In America, trophy hunters have been killing many top level carnivores like wolves, bears, mountain lions, and bobcats, all of which have essential value to their environments. Trophy hunters have killed over 78,000 mountain lions (also known as cougars or pumas) in the last twenty years. In January 2018, eastern mountain lions – who prowled North America, from Michigan to South Carolina – were officially declared extinct. Deer have no predators in many areas, and need constant culling to keep their numbers down. But when attempts are made to introduce natural predators such as wolves and coyotes, trophy hunters are the first to oppose it. Unfortunately, the trophy hunters are more interested in killing the bigger predatory animals, which is the antithesis of natural selection.

In 2015, SCI published a commissioned report by consultants Southwick Associates entitled *The Conservation Equation*. According to SCI, the report demonstrated that trophy hunting leads to the conservation of African wildlife and habitat in eight African countries. From their estimated 18,815 trophy hunt visits, they claimed the countries had received $426 million, and that trophy hunting supported directly and indirectly 53,000 jobs. In 2017, Humane Society International commissioned a report by consultants at Economists at Large (EAL) which found SCI's report to be flawed in the methodology used. The results of their report demonstrated that the economic benefits had been heavily overstated. Southwick claimed trophy hunting contributed $426 million, while EAL demonstrated a more realistic estimate of $132 million a year. Southwick claimed trophy hunting supported 53,000 jobs, but EAL said it was more likely in the range of 7,500-15,500 jobs. EAL also stated that the economic contribution of trophy hunters was at best 0.03% GDP, and that they made up less than 0.1% of tourists on average. Therefore, the adjusted Southwick's economic contribution of trophy hunting ($132 million or less) amounted to only 0.78% or less of the $17 billion in overall tourist spending, in the eight countries studied.

It's very difficult to see any form of trophy hunting as being beneficial to conservation, despite this being the key word in the hunting industry. In January 2014, a permit to kill a black rhinoceros in Namibia was auctioned off for $350,000. The Dallas Safari Club had hoped it would make $1,000,000, but public hostility to trophy hunters and the auction put a good number of bidders off. Dallas Safari Club stated that the purpose of the auction was to raise funds for the conservation of the black rhinoceros, as well as other endangered species. Members of the public and conservationists around the world were outraged by the auction. The highest bidder made quite a few appearances on talk shows, and said he had been shocked by the public outcry against the auction, and how he and his family had received a number of death threats.

It appears that the word 'conservation' means one thing to trophy hunters, and another thing entirely to those who don't hunt for pleasure. In essence, trophy hunters are using this term as an excuse to justify their sadistic behaviour, knowingly or unknowingly violating the very definition of this term by their actions. They also claim to be giving the meat from their kills to the poor in the local community, as well as providing income from their visits. They don't have a problem killing, because they think that the money paid for the privilege gives them the right to do what they do, and the locals are grateful for the revenue. On the contrary, research has shown that the money doesn't go to the locals, apart from the wages of a handful of men who help with the hunt. Instead, it goes to business owners, and to the government in the form of back handed payments. As for the meat, which is supposedly given to local people, it's just not enough – all this does is encourage the locals to go out and poach wildlife for themselves. After all, if rich Americans and Europeans can kill endangered and critical species for food, why can't they?

Another excuse for hunting endangered species, is that almost all the money from trophy hunters goes back into paying for anti-poaching teams and funding conservation. Hunters claim there are now more game animals than ever before in South Africa, and it's all thanks to their trophy hunting. But there are no statistics and proof to back any of this up. Hunters' claims are often empty, but they persist in the notion that what they do is in the name of conservation. They hold onto the belief that what they do is beneficial to others, as well as themselves and the trophy animals they harvest.

Is trophy hunting ethical?

In recent years, SCI has put more emphasis on their members giving out a good image of hunters to the world, but the stories in the media relating to individual trophy hunters beg to differ. One UK newspaper reported on a trophy hunter towards the end of 2017, with the headline *CONTROVERSIAL AND SICKENING: Trophy hunter kills elephants and rhinos without remorse…and says his only regret is how long it takes them to die.* The same trophy hunter had just shot a lion and was openly weeping, crying tears on the lion's majestic mane. The outpouring of emotion had nothing to do with the hunter's regret for the endangered animal he had just slaughtered. He was shedding tears of joy for finally achieving a lifelong ambition to slaughter a lion, one of the so-called "Big Five". In the BBC Four documentary "Trophy: The Big Game Hunting Controversy", the same trophy hunter is seen shooting an elephant. In a short interview in the film, the trophy hunter says he tries very hard to be ethical with the killing of animals, and it's upsetting for him to see the elephant in pain. He echoes what many trophy hunters claim, which is that he is an animal lover, but he sees no problem killing them for sport. He has no remorse and refers to the Bible:

God of my fathers, Lord of mercy, you …… you have made all things by your word, and in your wisdom have formed man to have dominion over the creatures you have made, and rule the world in holiness and justice.

WISDOM 9: 1 - 3

Like his fellow trophy hunters, this man is certain that when God mentioned men having dominion over all animals, it means animals were put on the earth for man to do what he wants with them. He recognises that other people have a heart for animals, and that he wants them to know he has the same heart, but just does things in a different way. Acknowledging that most people will never understand the heart of a true hunter, he firmly believes that what he does is helping wildlife. While critics see him as delusional, cruel, and arrogant, he says he doesn't care. Trophy hunters will constantly argue and deny that they are doing anything wrong, and state that they are doing it for the good of the animals, and for nature and conservation. Excuses range from, 'Killing an animal is a spiritual act of love' to 'Hunting puts you closer to God'. Well, for the majority of people in the world, it's not any of those things. Call it evil if you like, but it's nothing more than gratuitous butchery of wildlife, based on an industry's greed for money and the gross arrogance of the hunter.

A few last words ...

Trophy hunting is a worldwide business, which achieves nothing more than killing animals for recreational pleasure. It pushes some animal species towards extinction, in the most callous and brutal way. It's about time the world came together to stand up against this disgrace. It's time to end the suffering of the voiceless – the ones we should be protecting. There is no place on this planet for hunters, or those who kill for fun.

Charities to support and for further information

BORN FREE FOUNDATION   *Website: www.bornfree.org.uk*

Email: info@bornfree.org.uk   *Registered Charity No. 1070906*

"Born Free is opposed to the killing of any animal for sport or pleasure, and strongly refutes claims by trophy hunting proponents that their activities support conservation or local communities."

LEAGUE AGAINST CRUEL SPORTS   *Website: www.league.org.uk*

Email: info@league.org.uk   *Registered Charity: England & Wales 1095234*

Scotland SC045533

"The League believes this multi-million pound international industry is utterly unjustifiable from an animal welfare point of view but also for conservation reasons as it is pushing some of the world's most threatened species toward extinction."

IFAW (International Fund For Animal Welfare)   *Website: www.ifaw.org*

Registered Charity: IFAW is a 501(c)3 non-profit organisation.

"In order to achieve IFAW's vision of a world where animals are respected and protected we follow key principles in our hands approach with animals and in our advocacy work to secure better animal welfare protection in policy, legislation and society."

CHAPTER THREE
Elephants and Rhinos

"What we most need to do is to hear within us the sound of
the earth crying."

Thich Nhat Hanh

Tusks and horns

Poaching has devastated the world's population of elephants and rhinos, bringing some subspecies to the brink of extinction. The latest IUCN Red List, for species of both elephants and rhinos, ranged from vulnerable to critically endangered. This is not a new phenomenon, because poaching has been going on for centuries. But the world has to face facts – if poaching continues at the pace it has been going for the last 50 years, people reading this book will find that all wild elephants and rhinos will have disappeared from this planet during their lifetime.

It's estimated that 100 elephants in Africa are killed every day by poachers for their tusks. That's more or less one elephant every 15 minutes. In Asia, the estimate is 100 elephants killed a year, with about 50 of those killed by farmers to keep them away from their crops. Poaching is less common in India, because only some male elephants have tusks, and females don't have any. Regardless, the statistics are shocking.

How have we become so complacent? Illegal poaching in Africa and Asia has been highly publicised over the decades, on all forms of media. Ask anyone and they will be aware of illegal poaching and the effect it is having on the elephant and rhino populations. Yet it still goes on, and countries in Southeast Asia are still hungry for tusks and horns. We don't need ivory trinkets, and we certainly don't need to consume rhino horn to keep our bodies healthy. What we do need is a flourishing population of elephants and rhinos, playing vital roles in the ecosystem of their natural environments.

Illegal trade in wildlife body parts on the black market is an international, multi-billion dollar industry. It includes hundreds of animal species, and appears to be one of the main driving forces, or even the main driving force, towards the extinction of elephants and rhinos. So, what makes elephant tusks and rhino horns so valuable? The visible part of an elephant's tusk is made of ivory, which is made up of solid dentine with an outer layer of enamel. They are basically very long, continuously growing, front teeth. The hidden part of the tusk, which is roughly a third of the total length, is pulp cavity made up of tissue, blood, and nerves. Unlike rhinos, who can survive having their horn sawn off, elephants need to be killed in order for poachers to hack off their tusks. The bottom third of the tusk is embedded in the skull. Therefore, to take the tusk it must be hacked out of the skull, which would cause extreme pain to the elephant. Fully grown elephants are very dangerous when they feel threatened, so poachers always kill them before they attempt to take their tusks.

Over 70 per cent of illegal ivory finds its way to China and Vietnam. The tusk of an elephant can be worth $1,500 per pound in weight on the black market. Given that a single tusk can weigh 250 pounds, and the average yearly pay of a worker in Sub-Saharan Africa is less than $1,500, poaching can be a risk worthwhile. Elephant tusks used for ivory carvings can be traced back 35,000 years, so ivory carving is embedded in the culture in Asian countries. Ivory is a material that can be carved without splintering, and is suitable and practical for many uses. Lots of things have been made from ivory, such as sculptures, dagger handles, buttons, piano keys, combs, chopsticks, billiard balls, jewellery, trinkets, and so on. Today, ivory can be replaced by plastic, but widespread use of this is only going to add to the slow degradation rates of plastics in the biosphere. There are also natural materials to consider, like shells and bones. In the Amazon region, the Jarina seed is used for artistic work, because of its mechanical properties and appearance that resembles elephant ivory. Given the information and intelligence of what we already know, how can anyone demand a piece of art made in ivory today – especially when it means the inevitable extinction of the planet's largest land mammal?

Similarly, three rhinos are killed on average every day, for their horns. Two species of rhino, the Javan rhino and the Sumatran rhino, are on the brink of extinction. One subspecies, the northern white rhino, is functionally extinct, with only two females left on the planet. Neither of the females can become pregnant. Instead, scientists have been able to fertilise the rhino eggs with frozen sperm from male northern white rhinos, who previously walked on this planet. Once fertilised, the eggs become pre-embryos, and can be placed in the uteruses of a similar subspecies – the southern white rhino females. Here they can develop and hopefully give birth to northern rhino babies. Other subspecies of rhino are classified as endangered or critically endangered. Rhinos have been roaming the planet for the last 50 million years, yet the last ones are being slaughtered just so some wealthy people can boast to their peers about how much money they have – by offering them rhino horn powder mixed with alcohol or water: 'Hey, drink this rhino horn stuff! We can get drunk tonight but we won't have a hangover in the morning!' Yet rhino horn is made of keratin – the same as human nails. So, we could just as well chew on our fingernails, which equates to no monetary cost and thriving rhino populations in the wild.

Like ivory, the greatest demand for rhino horn comes from China and Vietnam. Rhino horn has been used in traditional Chinese medicine for more than 2,000 years. It's normally used to treat fever, rheumatism, gout, cancer, impotence, and hangovers.

It also has a reputation for curing snakebites, typhoid, headaches, food poisoning, hallucinations, carbuncles, vomiting, and demonic possession. The Vietnamese seem happy to use it as an aphrodisiac too, as well as believing it has other benefits. In Vietnam, there are many wildlife products recognised as valuable and rare, but rhino horn is the most coveted. Rhinos are seen as unconquerable and the strongest animal in nature. Most people are aware that the rhinos are being killed for their horns, but they feel very disconnected from this. In fact, they don't see themselves as being responsible for the demise of the rhino, and if the species is lost forever they will not be affected personally – so they don't care.

In the last 12 months, Kenya has been quoted as introducing the death penalty for convicted wildlife poachers, but this information appears to have been misconstrued. Kenya's tourism minister has advocated stiffer punishments for poachers, and has said that current penalties are not proportionate to the damage caused by poachers. Under the *Wildlife Conservation and Management Act 2013*, poachers convicted for serious violations towards endangered species in Kenya can be handed a life sentence, but not the death penalty. No death row prisoner has been executed since 1987, and there has been no plan to introduce the death penalty for poachers. In recent years, poaching in Kenya has seen a significant decline, which has been due to increased conservation efforts and more motivated law enforcement. According to the Ministry of Tourism and Wildlife in Kenya, there has been a decline by 78 per cent in elephant poaching, and 85 per cent in rhino poaching, compared to statistics in 2013.

Organised crime syndicates are partly responsible for large scale poaching of elephants and rhinos – often providing poachers with the high-powered technology and weaponry to kill many animals at once. It's very easy to get guns in Africa. Official stockpiles of seized weapons often find their way into the hands of those who require them. The military have used state issued guns to carry out illegal killings, and there are also people willing to trade guns in return for ivory. Experienced poachers prefer hunting rifles, for their long range and their ability to take down an elephant or rhino with a single shot. However, assault rifles and machine guns are becoming popular, especially amongst organised poaching factions, and these can be cheaper to buy than hunting rifles. But, not all poachers use guns. Rhinos can be darted, poisoned, or trapped with snares. Sometimes their horns are hacked from their heads with machetes or chainsaws, whilst they're still alive. They usually die a slow, agonising death whilst their young watch from nearby – helpless.

Why are elephants special?

"The elephant intrigues me so much, its strength and dignity, its silent movement and sudden trumpeting fury, the humour of its young, the threatening beauty of its tusks, the delicate touch of its trunk and the intelligent look in its wise old eye – all these enthralled me." **George Adamson**

Elephants live in pronounced and established families. The oldest and largest female elephant, known as the matriarch, takes the lead over her daughters and their offspring. Sometimes, unrelated females are allowed to join the herd. The male bulls have a functional role, which is to breed and increase the elephant population in his territory. Young males stay with their mother until they are about 14 years old. It was originally thought that the males went off into the bush and led a lonely life, but now we know that they wander from family to family. As the males grow older, they mix with other males of different ages, playing rough and learning from the older ones. This way, they begin to understand their own strength, and learn the tactics they will need to use as they mature.

The elephant family provides a coherent and social structure in which young elephants can grow and develop their skills for adulthood. They are taught normal behaviour in a social and caring context from their mothers, relatives, and friends. Young elephants emulate the behaviour of adults and learn food foraging skills. Family members serve as a defence barrier against predators and other dangers. This environment of learning ensures a shield against inappropriate behaviour, such as aggression by males towards females and calves. Elephants help each other in times of distress. They feel emotions, just like humans, and they grieve for their dead. It's interesting that there are cultural differences and practices by elephants in different areas. Where elephants live near farmlands, the art of dismantling electric fences seems to be normal for most elephants in the herd. Studies of various elephant herds have shown different behaviours and reactions that have been specific to only one herd or herds in the same ranges.

Elephants are empathetic souls, and they have frequently been observed as recognising and responding to another elephant's pain or problem. They assist one another, whether that's helping babies climb out of pools with slippery banks, or helping an injured elephant that has been darted, attacked, or wounded. They call out in distress to attract the other members of the herd to help, and they have been seen comforting each other. They even display grieving rituals when members of their herd die. Elephants have complex brains, which are so multifaceted that they are capable of remembering, learning, experiencing, and communicating. So, do they understand what we humans are doing to them, and how they are being pushed to the edge of extinction? They have witnessed the mass slaughter of family members by poachers for their tusks, and the senseless killing by trophy hunters for their body parts. We have taken away their habitat and their historical ranges. Now, we are taking away their souls and their physical existence on the planet.

How many wild elephants are left across the world today?

African elephant	Savanna elephant	c 415,000	Vulnerable
	Forest elephant	c 40,000	Vulnerable
Asian elephant	Indian elephant	20,000 – 25,000	Endangered
	Sri Lankan elephant	2,500 – 4,000	Endangered
	Sumatran elephant	2,400 – 2,800	Critically Endangered

African savanna elephant

During the rainy season, the African savanna elephant is a familiar sight on the vast expanse of grassland dotted with acacia trees. They are the largest species of elephant living in eastern and southern Africa, and the largest land mammal in the world. Their very large ears keep them cool, flapping backwards to dispel the heat. Sometimes family units join together to form "clans", and they can number up to several hundred elephants. Significant populations can be found in Botswana, Tanzania, Zimbabwe, Kenya, and South Africa. They are usually confined to well-protected areas, but less than 20 per cent of the Savanna elephant's habitat is actually under "formal" protection. Why is that?

Elephants sometimes travel up to 50 miles or more a day, crossing national borders from one country to another. Some countries have better protection laws for elephants than others. So, if an elephant is wandering around in Angola in the morning, it will have much greater protection under international law than it will later on in the day, when it might cross over to Botswana. The future requires cooperation between countries to help support these elephants. The Convention on International Trade in Endangered Species of Wild Fauna and Flora (CITES) continues to focus on the sovereignty of each country in regulating trade of wildlife. But this is madness – three-quarters of the world's elephant population are spread across one or more national borders. This means that elephants are getting varying levels of protection against the ivory trade – which means that the overall protection is inconsistent with ecological reality and conservational best practice.

CITES is one of the most important international treaties for protecting elephants from poachers. Where elephants are listed on Appendix I in 33 countries, it means elephants have the highest level of protection, as the ivory trade is totally banned in these countries. But Botswana, Namibia, South Africa, and Zimbabwe have their elephants on Appendix II. This listing calls for a temporary nine-year moratorium on the re-opening of the ivory trade. Whilst this was still in place, Namibia and Zimbabwe applied to CITES to have the ivory trade restrictions lifted. That request was denied. In January 2019, Namibia submitted proposals again to allow international commercial trade in live animals, hunting trophies, and the sale of raw ivory to consumer countries. Namibia is also wanting to down-list its rhinos to Appendix II. At the same time, nine African countries proposed for the African elephants of Botswana, Namibia, South Africa, and Zimbabwe to be up-listed to Appendix I, in view of the insatiable onslaught of poaching activities. Then, Zambia wanted to propose down-listing its elephants to Appendix II, in order to export ivory to consumer countries. Botswana, Namibia, Zimbabwe, and South Africa already have their elephants on Appendix II, and they are pushing to weaken the same restrictions they have signed up to. Up down, up down! How is this helping the conservation of elephants and rhinos? Where do the profits go in the countries pushing for the legal trade in ivory, allowing trophy hunting to kill endangered species, and exporting wildlife to other countries for the captive industry? The proposals that have been submitted by African countries are up for consideration at the next World Wildlife Conference. This is the eighteenth meeting of the Conference of Parties to the CITES, which will be heard in May-June 2019 in Sri Lanka. Meanwhile, in February 2019, Zimbabwe forcibly separated 35 young savanna elephants from their mothers in the wild, to be flown to zoos in China. These young elephants were reported to be babies, with some only around two years old. Rangers flew helicopters close to the herds to frighten and panic the young elephants away from their mothers and the rest of the herd. Whilst the youngsters were being loaded into trucks, the helicopters flew closely round the herd to prevent the elephants from trying to protect their young. During the Mugabe era, Zimbabwe's wildlife was frequently sold to Asia and the Middle East, to settle debts. There has been no change there, and these activities have blackened Zimbabwe's reputation as a tourist destination. The fate of the 35 young elephants is unknown. But it shows just how contemptible this kind of trade is, even though it is completely legal under CITES.

African forest elephant

These elephants inhabit the densely wooded rainforests of west and central Africa. They are an elusive subspecies of African elephants, and are sometimes called the "forgotten elephants". Forest elephants are smaller than savanna elephants. They have more oval-shaped ears, and their tusks are straighter and point downwards, unlike the tusks of savanna elephants which are more curved in shape. Forest elephant tusks are also denser and harder, with a pinkish tinge; therefore they are more desirable to carvers of ivory. The harder ivory allows for more intricate carving. These elephants are rarely filmed or photographed, because they are hard to locate within their dense habitat. Estimating their population numbers is difficult, because counting methods tend to depend on visual identification. With poaching on the increase, it's believed that as many as ten per cent of forest elephants are being killed each year. About 62 per cent of forest elephants have been killed for their ivory by poachers in the last decade. Unfortunately, the real number is all guesswork. Only now are scientists beginning to understand the forest elephant's habits, group structures, movements, and diet. This is the information required to help conservation efforts protect the forest elephants, but it may have come too late. The forest elephants are facing extinction more quickly than had previously been assumed. It takes more than 20 years for female forest elephants to give birth, and then they only give birth once every five to six years. This reproduction rate is about three times slower than that of savanna elephants, and cannot keep up with the pace of shameless poaching and loss of habitat.

Gabon, with about 88 per cent of its land still covered in forest, is home to about 50-60 per cent of the remaining 40,000 African forest elephants. Current statistics show that a dozen forest elephants a day are being killed by heavily armed poachers in Gabon. In order to combat this, the British army have been training 850 park guards in the 13 national parks across Gabon. The park guards have had to become more militarised, because the poachers were shooting them. The Democratic Republic of Congo has lost 95% of its forest elephant population in the last ten years. The trade in ivory is linked to criminal syndicates, who are also successfully smuggling gold and guns. They are even smuggling people, and there is evidence that some of the profits from ivory are being directed back to the African Islamic terrorists known as Boko Haram. Winning the war against poachers and their criminal syndicates is vital for local communities, wildlife, national security, and global security.

Asian Indian elephant

The wild Indian elephant population can be found throughout Southeast Asia, in countries like India, Bangladesh, Bhutan, Cambodia, Laos, Malaysia, Myanmar, China, Nepal, Pakistan, Thailand, and Vietnam. There are several key differences between Indian elephants and African elephants – with the primary difference being that Indian elephants have smaller ears than African elephants. There are other differences too – the African elephant has a two-fingered tip to its trunk, whilst the Indian elephant has a one fingered tip. Also, Indian elephants tend to be smaller than their African cousins. But there is one interesting difference, which goes further than physical appearance. Genetic research has found that Asian elephants are more closely related to the woolly mammoth than African elephants. The Indian elephant has been domesticated for around 4,000 years now, serving mankind, where it is generally considered that African elephants are too dangerous or just too wild to ride on. There are a few places in Africa where they can be ridden, but it is rare. The Indian elephant, on the other hand, has been highly valued by Asian culture over thousands of years. They are taken from the wild to be domesticated, and used as transportation, as well as for moving heavy objects like tree trunks in the logging industry. Nearly all the elephants in zoos and circuses around the world are Indian elephants. This is because they are more amenable to training and working than their African counterparts.

Ivory poaching is not as extensive and large-scale for Indian elephants as it is for African elephants. The tusks of the Indian elephant are smaller, and the females usually don't have them. In fact, only 25-30 per cent of male Indian elephants have tusks. Does this make Indian elephants less vulnerable to ivory poachers? Unfortunately not. Some ivory carvers insist that ivory from Indian elephants is of a higher quality, but whether this is true or just perceived to be true doesn't matter – it is creating a demand for Indian elephant ivory. This is unfortunate for the species. Because the females don't usually have tusks, there is a serious imbalance in the ratio of deaths between male and female elephants. With less males, there is a significant impact on reproduction, and a decline in the genetic diversity of the elephants to provide a healthy population. It has also resulted in a growing regularity of male elephants being born without tusks.

In Myanmar, market investigators from the TRAFFIC wildlife monitoring network found elephant skin for sale. In 2006, they found four pieces for sale. Then, in 2009 they found 278, and by 2014 they counted more than 1,200 pieces for sale. Dried elephant skin has traditionally been ground into a powder, and then mixed with oil and elephant fat to make a paste. It's supposed to help skin problems like eczema and fungal infections. However, wildlife traffickers have created a new purpose for elephant skin – they are using it to create jewellery and other trinkets. Dried skin is polished into small, translucent beads, which increase in value based on the amount of visible red blood vessels. If more elephant skin is coming to the markets in Myanmar, then poaching of Indian elephants has to be on the rise. Many elephant carcasses have been found stripped of skin, often so mutilated that researchers couldn't say whether they were male or female. Nearly all the elephants were tuskless, so they hadn't been killed for their ivory.

Catching wild elephants for captivity is, in effect, poaching. The poachers often target baby elephants who can end up in zoos, and are more trainable for tourist attractions – where they are trained to give rides and entertainment to holiday travellers. Sadly, elephants can be very protective of their babies, and poachers often have to kill the elephant mothers, and sometimes other adults from the herd too, in order to secure the baby elephants. Capturing an elephant in the wild is not an easy task, and methods range from darting or lassoing single elephants, to driving herds up against purpose-built barriers. This is extremely stressful for the elephants, and scientists believe it causes long-term psychological damage, which is responsible for shortening elephants' lives in captivity. Captured elephants are usually sold in auctions or elephant markets. Buyers are usually from the logging industry, overseers of temples, or the tourist industry. They often bring astrologers with them to look for promising signs from the elephants for their buyers. These signs are believed to indicate temperament, health, longevity, and work ethic.

Unfortunately, elephants kept in captivity are worked hard. They are expensive to keep and consume enormous amounts of food and water. Some temples used to keep their own elephants, but now they are more likely to hire them from mahouts (an elephant keeper) when they need them. The logging industry in Myanmar still uses elephants too. It exports 75 per cent of the world's teak; approximately 50-60 per cent of the country's population relies on the forestry for their basic needs. The elephants live in forest camps and are owned by large companies. They have people (oozies) to tend to their daily needs, and government veterinarians who carry out regular health checks.

At night, the elephants forage in family groups in the forest, unsupervised. In contrast, elephants used by illegal logging ventures are often brutally treated.

Indian elephants are used to carry tourists on safaris, who are looking for tigers and rhinos. They also carry tourists to particular spots, and on elephant treks. In countries like Thailand, elephants are used as attractions for tourists, who will pay for selfies whilst riding them, washing them, patting their trunks, or hugging baby elephants. Elephants can also be forced to entertain tourists by playing football, painting, riding tricycles, throwing darts, and dancing. Researchers from World Animal Protection (WAP) have discovered that this has encouraged people to take more elephants from the wild. After assessing more than 3,000 elephants in the tourist industry in Thailand, they found that more than 75 per cent were living in "severely cruel" conditions. Zoos across the world keep Indian elephants in inadequate environments. Many are kept cooped up in tiny areas, and some are literally chained with little or no exercise. They suffer from arthritis, major foot problems, and premature death. Those elephants kept in circuses are also cooped up and chained. They are also subject to cruel methods of training, but luckily more and more countries around the world are banning wild animals from performing in circuses.

In the wild, the Indian elephant faces fierce competition for resources. The continent of Asia is so densely populated that people and animals in the wild are competing for the same space. The elephants' habitat is shrinking at a catastrophic pace, with historical migration routes being cut off, and fragmentation forcing the elephants onto agricultural land and human settlements. Human-elephant conflicts are on the rise, as elephants raid farm crops, damage buildings, and hurt or kill people. Electrified fencing is possibly the only way to keep elephants away from villages and farm crops. Yet there are some elephants who have learnt ways of overcoming these barriers. People use flares to scare away the elephants. Again, elephants learn not to be scared of the flares after they have witnessed them a few times. A hungry elephant can overcome most deterrents, in order to get food. They particularly like sugar cane, bananas, and fruit, though they will happily eat anything edible – including stores of rice.

This is a particularly difficult problem to solve from the point of conservation – as Indian elephants, who are identified as endangered, are being killed in retaliation.

Asian Sri Lankan elephant

The small island of Sri Lanka is densely populated. Though its elephants are listed as endangered, with 2,500-4,000 elephants in the wild, it is the country with the highest density of elephants in the world. The primary threat to Sri Lanka's elephants is deforestation and the ensuing human settlements and agriculture. During the 25-year civil war between the Sinhalese and Tamils, many elephant herds moved into areas that humans had abandoned. Now, in times of peace, those areas have been reallocated to humans – who are building residential settlements and clearing land for agriculture. The result is that elephants are being driven into smaller areas, making their ranges more fragmented. The elephant population in Sri Lanka has fallen by 65% since the end of the nineteenth century.

Sri Lankan elephants hold symbolic and cultural importance, and are commonly used in ceremonial occasions like Buddhist festivals. These days, they are less likely to be used in logging activities, and instead play an important role in ecotourism for Sri Lanka. There are a number of national parks, where elephants can be seen in their natural environment, giving tourists unforgettable experiences. But the elephant orphanages are nothing more than profit making ventures that are using and abusing elephants of all ages. Most of the elephants are chained. When they are taken to the river for tourist photographs, the chains are below the water level, hidden from the photos. Reviews describe the experience, saying the elephants look underfed and miserable, and are often poked with hook sticks and shouted at. Many tourists feel sad and angry, and cannot wait to leave, citing how awful the experience was and how it was a financial rip off.

Asian Sumatran elephant

The critically endangered Sumatran elephant shares many of the survival problems that affect critically endangered Sumatran tigers, Sumatran orangutans, and Sumatran rhinos. Sumatra's wood and paper product industries, alongside oil palm, coffee, sugar, and rubber plantations, are responsible for some of the world's most egregious deforestation. Over two thirds of Sumatra's natural lowland forest has been cleared in the last 25 years. This has caused local extinctions of elephants in many places. It has been estimated that 80 per cent of the elephant population has declined during that period, leaving small herds confined in scanty forest areas, where they probably won't survive in the wild for very long.

The Sumatran elephant has shorter tusks than the other elephant species. The females have smaller tusks than the males, which have either tiny tusks or no tusks at all. Yet poachers will still attempt to kill them, to make money on the illegal ivory market. Poachers also set snares in the forest to capture animals for bushmeat, such as wild pigs or deer. These traps often catch other species in the forest, and that can include elephants, particularly baby ones. The traps are set near watering holes and well-trodden routes through the forest. The snare is usually a long piece of wire, with a loop at the end attached to a tree or log. The loop hangs from a branch or small tree, and the purpose is for the snare to catch an animal by the neck as it is walking along the trail.

Illegal logging causes a huge problem for Indonesia. As much as 40-60 per cent of deforestation is carried out illegally, though various sources have quoted even higher percentages. These tropical rainforests have a unique biodiversity, which is key to the future of critically endangered species. Clearing rainforest devastates wildlife habitat and can infringe on elephant migratory routes. This problem is multiplied by the expansion and development of residential areas – which infringe on animals' habitats and ultimately fragment elephants' territories.

We must save elephants

Elephants have been on our planet for 55 million years. By studying fossils, scientists have discovered that over 300 species of elephants have walked across the earth. Elephants were once the dominant species throughout most of Africa and India, but they have steadily declined as the human population has increased. The number of elephants and their historical ranges have decreased at an alarming rate over the last 100 years, thanks to human activity. Humans require land: to farm, build roads, construct residential villages and towns, and develop mines and plantations – this is all shrinking the terrain for elephants to survive in the wild. More African elephants are being slaughtered at the hands of poachers than are being born, and time is running out to save them.

As a keystone species, elephants create and maintain the ecosystems which not only enable other elephants to thrive, but countless plant and animal species to survive too. If elephants disappear off the face of our planet, then it will gravely impact innumerable plants and animals, and the fundamental habitat for biodiversity throughout Africa and Asia. If we lose elephants, we not only lose the largest living land mammal that we have admired and loved from childhood, but we lose an environmental caretaker for our planet. We have so much more to learn from elephants, and we need to do so much more to protect and conserve them.

Rhinos

"No one in the world needs a rhino horn but a rhino."

Paul Oxton

All five species of rhino in the world today are threatened with extinction. They have survived on this planet for 50 million years, but they are struggling to survive the immense slaughter of hunting, wanton poaching of their horns, and the loss of their precious habitat by humans in the last 130 years or so. The decline in rhino populations began when European powers began to colonise Africa. As land was cleared for agriculture, plantations, and urban developments, natural habitats began to suffer. Gun-toting European settlers and wealthy Americans caused senseless loss of wildlife, with their flamboyant safaris and mass hunting. Teddy Roosevelt himself, former president of the United States, went on an African safari with his son. This was heavily publicised as a scientific expedition, but Roosevelt was out to kill every African animal he encountered. Included in his haul of 296 large animals, Roosevelt annihilated: 13 rhinos, 8 elephants, 9 lions, 15 zebras, 8 warthogs, a crocodile, 5 wildebeests, 6 monkeys, 2 ostriches, and 3 pythons. His son managed to wipe out 216 specimens of similar large animals. Roosevelt is still worshipped as a hero of trophy hunting today. Today's trophy hunters still blatantly claim to be conservationists and saviours of wild animals, though many species have been wiped off the planet since Roosevelt's time. How anyone who thinks preserving wildlife is done through slaughtering, skinning, stuffing, posing for photos and selfies with dead carcasses, and then taking them home to hang on your wall, is beyond belief. In Roosevelt's time, there was probably an abundance of animals to kill – although that's not to say it was moral or ethical for him to do so. He was out there to show off, impressing people around the world. In the present day (and in Roosevelt's time too), it's nothing short of criminal to engage as a trophy hunter, when much of our precious wildlife is becoming endangered and on the brink of extinction.

The demand for rhino horn and other body parts is not just limited to Southeast Asia. Both rhino species in Africa have faced extinction before. In the 1800s, the southern white rhino was nearly hunted to extinction by European settlers, sport hunters, and opportunists cashing in on the rhino horn trade. Powdered rhino horn is believed to treat fever, impotence, cancer, and hangovers. The key word is "believed", because rhino horn has not been proven to cure any of these problems. Rhino horn is actually made of keratin, which is the same substance as our fingernails and hair strands. One could propose that people could cut their nails and hair, and use them to cure cancer, impotence, and fever along with their hangovers – but of course most people would label this ridiculous. So why do they believe the same nonsense about rhino horn? If people stopped listening to these myths, it would not only allow the planet's wild rhino population to thrive, but it would save those buying rhino horn a great deal of money.

How many wild rhinos are left across the world today?

White Rhino	Northern white rhino	2 (females)	Functionally Extinct
	Southern white rhino	19,682 – 21,077	Near Threatened
Black Rhino		5,042 - 5,455	Critically Endangered
Great One-Horned Rhino		3,500 – 3,600	Vulnerable
Sumatran Rhino (extinct in the wild)		Less than 80	Critically Endangered
Javan Rhino (extinct in the wild)		No more than 69	Critically Endangered

Northern white rhino

The northern white rhino is possibly the most endangered wild mammal on earth – there are only two females left on the planet. The subspecies is therefore listed as functionally extinct. They were once extremely common in Central Africa, but thanks to illegal hunting for horns, the northern white rhino became extinct in the wild. In March 2018, the last male northern white rhino – named Sudan – was euthanised at the age of 45 years. He had been suffering from "age related complications". Sudan was the last of the northern white rhinos to have been born in the wild. He was translocated to a Czech zoo, and then brought back to Kenya in 2009 along with the other two remaining females and a male that died in 2014. All four rhinos had been living under armed, 24-hour protection from rangers, to keep them safe from poachers.

Both the remaining females, Najin and Fatu, are not capable of bearing calves. Najin has achilles tendon problems, meaning her legs are not strong enough to support the weight of an unborn calf. Fatu is barren, because of a past infection in her uterus. However, scientists have managed to extract eggs from them, which can be implanted in female southern white rhinos. Over the years, semen has been collected from Sudan as well as from four other captive northern white rhinos. Scientists are confident that they can save the northern white rhino, by using in vitro fertilisation techniques – impregnating southern white rhinos with embryos made from the sperm of northern white males who are now dead. Testing has been carried out at the San Diego Zoo Institute for Conservation Research on 6 female southern white rhinos, and one is pregnant. It's hard to believe that there is hope for this subspecies of rhino. Thankfully, scientists are confident that they have the knowledge, and believe they can produce a viable population of northern whites for the future.

Southern white rhino

The southern white rhino is perhaps the least endangered subspecies of African rhinos today, and this is largely thanks to successful conservation efforts. These rhinos are mainly found across four countries: South Africa, Namibia, Zimbabwe, and Kenya, with the large majority living in South Africa. In the late nineteenth century, they were thought to be extinct. Then, in 1895, a small population of less than 100 rhinos were discovered in South Africa. Today they are classified as near threatened, and have the highest population numbers of all the species of rhino on the planet. Southern white rhinos can be found in protected areas and private game reserves, numbering about 20,000 in total as a species.

Behind the elephant, the southern white rhino (along with the greater one-horned rhino), is probably the second largest land mammal in the world. They can live in small groups of up to seven individuals, but they are usually solitary animals. They have poor eyesight and have difficulty detecting someone standing only a hundred feet away – if the person stays still. But they make up for it with their acute sense of hearing and smell. White rhinos tend to thrive in open savanna and grassland, and they eat nothing but grass. They operate as "select lawnmowers", helping to maintain the vast grasslands and selecting to graze on certain grass species – thereby promoting biodiversity. This herbivorous grazer has just one enemy, and that is man. Humans are their only threat. Poaching has threatened rhinos for centuries, and trophy hunting nearly drove the white rhinos to extinction in the nineteenth century. After a successful comeback from the end of that century, they are now threatened again, with their numbers decreasing each day thanks to poaching and loss of habitat. They are relatively unaggressive animals, and an easy target. It's ironic that the southern white rhino is the most common rhino in the world, and yet it is still not safe from extinction. In order to protect rhinos, there has been a change in policy that has allowed private ownership of wildlife in South Africa and some other African countries. In most nations around the world, wildlife is owned by the state. African wildlife is a matter of great international concern. In the last 30 years, Zimbabwe, Namibia, and South Africa have changed their legal regimes to give full control over the use of wildlife to private owners of the land where wildlife is located. Previously, private owners were not interested in increasing wildlife populations on their land, because there were no incentives to do so – the state had denied them the full opportunity to make profits from wildlife. The privatisation of wildlife management in South Africa has thrived, with wildlife tourism and wildlife ranches. Hence, the largest population of southern white rhino reside in South Africa. The private owners are also responsible for their own rhinos' protection. It has been a great success, but keeping wild animals and breeding them on ranches for profit doesn't sit easy with many conservationists and individuals.

Black rhino

The black rhino is smaller than the white rhino. It has two horns, with the front one being longer than the other. The front horn generally measures up to 50 centimetres in length. Depending on various factors, black rhino horns can be of different shapes and sizes. Generally, males tend to have thicker horns, and females tend to have longer, thinner horns. This species of rhino are browsers, which means they eat woody plants like trees, bushes, and shrubs. To help them eat, they have a hooked upper lip, which enables them to pluck leaves and fruit from the branches. Black rhinos are not actually black, but a grey colour. The species has probably derived that name as a means of distinguishing it from the white rhino – which is also grey.

There are four subspecies of the black rhino: the southern central, the eastern, the south western, and the western. In 2011, the western black rhino was declared extinct. At the end of the eighteenth century, European settlers hunted them relentlessly. The black rhino experienced the worst decline in total numbers of all the rhino species. They were once found throughout sub-Saharan Africa, and were so plentiful that even though they were solitary animals it was not unusual to come across 20 or more in a single day. By the end of the 1960s, they had been wiped out or near annihilated from a number of African countries. At the beginning of the 1970s, the black rhino population was estimated to be around 70,000. Around the same time, a poaching epidemic was in full swing. It successfully eliminated 96 per cent of the black rhinos outside and inside conservation areas within national parks and game reserves. By 1993, there were only 2,300 black rhinos surviving in the wild. Fortunately, the black rhino has slowly recovered, largely thanks to conservation and anti-poaching efforts. There are now around 5,000 black rhinos in the wild.

Today, about 98 per cent of black rhinos are distributed in mainly four countries: South Africa, Zimbabwe, Namibia, and Kenya. The remaining 2 per cent can be found in Swaziland, Tanzania, Zambia, Botswana, and Malawi. They have been reintroduced to Zambia and Botswana, after previously being wiped out from these two countries. Sadly, illegal poaching remains a threat.

Greater one-horned rhino

The greater one-horned rhino, often referred to as the "Indian rhino", is the largest of the rhino species. Sometimes referred to as the "plated rhino", it has folds of skin that look like armour. As the name suggests, it only has a single horn. During the early part of the twentieth century, the greater one-horned rhino had a population of fewer than 200. Today, there are approximately 3,500 in the wild, in northern India and southern Nepal, and this is largely thanks to strict protection from Indian and Nepalese wildlife authorities. Greater one-horned rhinos are listed as vulnerable on IUCN's Red List. Found in grasslands and wetlands, they can spend 60 per cent of the day submerged in water, with just their nose and ear tips showing above the surface. They can even feed under water.

Protection for this vulnerable species is down to a tremendous collaboration between local communities, conservation partners, governments, and law enforcement authorities in India and Nepal. When drones were first introduced in Assam's Kaziranga National Park, they were hailed as a 'milestone in wildlife protection'. It was possible to keep an eye on the remotest areas of the 480 square kilometre park, and deter poachers who now had to reckon with surveillance from the air. The drones were also useful for keeping an eye on unauthorised settlements within the park, which were often linked to poaching.

The State of Assam successfully put aside four areas to conserve and protect India's Greater one-horned rhino. These are the Pobitora Wildlife Sanctuary, the Orang

National Park, the Kaziranga National Park, and the Manas National Park. Now the rhinos within Assam's four reserves are also suffering from the impact of invasive plants. These plants are currently forcing out native plants, smothering the vegetation that the rhinos depend on for food. Parthenium is one such example. This a plant native to the Americas, and an alien species to India. It has a history of damaging local ecosystems, and its harmful impact has been seen in more than 20 countries around the world. In order to combat this, mechanical removal methods, such as hand weeding, have been attempted. Hand weeding is the simplest way to deal with the issue, but it's labour intensive, expensive, and has to be repeated consistently. Less laborious options, like controlled burning and spraying chemicals, could have disastrous results on the rhino and other wildlife.

Nepal's anti-poaching success comes from their exceptional efforts in protecting their rhinos. About 600 rhinos in this rugged and mountainous country have generous support from authorities. This is particularly encouraging, as many governments and local authorities are often rife with corruption, and don't necessarily make conservation a priority. The value that the Nepalese put on their wild heritage is commendable, and Nepal is a wonderful role model for many other countries.

Sumatran rhino

In 1986, it was thought that around 800 Sumatran rhinos remained in the wild across Southeast Asia. This included rhinos in Bhutan, northeast India, southern China, Malaysia, Cambodia, and Thailand. Thirty years later, they can only be found in ten isolated and fragmented pockets of habitat in Borneo and Sumatra. Official estimates advise there are fewer than 100 Sumatran rhinos in the wild, but some experts think there could be as few as 30. They live in remote places, where sightings are very rare. Therefore, it is not surprising that population estimates are disputed. Sumatran rhinos are predicted to become extinct in our lifetime, and were declared extinct in Malaysia in 2015. Their only hope is in the ambitious plan launched by the Indonesian government and international conservationist organisations, to bring the Sumatran rhino back from the brink of extinction.

The Sumatran rhino is the smallest of the five rhino species, and has two horns. It is also the hairiest, which is why it's seen as the closest living relative to the legendary woolly rhino that lived in Europe and Asia during the Ice Age. Apart from the hair, it also has other prehistoric characteristics that link it to its primitive relatives. Sumatran rhinos lived at liberty in the dense tropical forests until 1930, when people started hunting them for their horns. These horns were traded with the Chinese in exchange for porcelain objects. Over the decades, poaching increased, as did deforestation, and the Sumatran rhino population began to dwindle dramatically.

Back in the 1980s, a captive breeding plan was introduced to help save the Sumatran rhino. Lots of things went wrong, and this plan was somewhat of a disaster for about 20 years, before they managed to achieve success. Scientists couldn't get the females to become pregnant, and for the first 17 years there were no births. Other things went wrong too, such as injuries during capture, inadequate feeding in captivity, disease, and illness. When wild populations dwindle to such an extent, captive breeding is a viable strategy for saving the species. However, in order to commence captive breeding, there are many challenges to overcome. Tracking down and capturing animals of suitable age and gender in the wild takes time and effort. Relocating animals from the wild into captivity can be a risky and unpredictable task. Wild animals take time to settle in their new environment, and there is no way of knowing in advance if they will have a successful coupling, or if advanced reproduction methods will work. It's a long and complex journey to care for the remaining animals. Until the threats to their habitat have been dealt with, and the population is large enough to survive in the wild, some species and subspecies must remain in captivity.

The government of Indonesia, with a coalition of conservation organisations and experts, has embarked on an international effort to bring back the Sumatran rhino from the brink of extinction. Their first task was to capture a female in the wild, to join the breeding programme. These animals are shy and elusive, living in the dense forests of Borneo. A pit trap was set up to capture a female in April 2018. It was 8 months before a female rhino stepped into it, and they named her "Pahu". Due to their fragmented habitat, which is separated by mountainous terrain, the Sumatran rhino have a hard time finding mating partners. With the species in crisis, everything now rests on the success of captive breeding.

Javan rhino

The Javan rhino is the rarest of the rhino species still existing in the world today. With a population of less than 69 rhinos, they survive in Indonesia's Ujung Kulon National Park, heavily protected by armed rhino protection units. By working in partnership with local people and rhino conservationists, the Indonesian government has been successful in preventing poachers from poaching further rhinos. Incredibly, a rhino has not been poached in the park since 1999.

In the past, Javan rhinos were commonly seen throughout Southeast Asia. They could be found from near Calcutta in India, across Bangladesh, southern China, Myanmar, Vietnam, Thailand, Cambodia, Laos, Malaysia, the western side of Java, and Sumatra. Today, the species is on the verge of extinction, and there are no Javan rhinos in captivity. Outside of the population in Ujung Kulon National Park, the last remaining Javan rhino was found dead in Cat Tien National Park, Vietnam in 2010. Sadly, it had been shot, with its horn hacked from its head. During 2011, the Javan rhino was officially declared extinct in Vietnam.

Javan rhinos can live in a variety of habitats, like coastal swamps and mountainous regions, but they probably thrive best in tropical forests – where they have access to grassy glades. A good part of their day is spent wallowing in mud holes. It's important for them to keep cool and out of the sun, to rehydrate their skin and for getting rid of biting insects and ectoparasites that live on their bodies. Unfortunately, only 40% of the territory in Ujung Kulon National Park is considered to be suitable for the Javan rhinos. It has been declared that Ujung Kulon is close to carrying capacity, and that it cannot sustain a further increase in the rhino numbers. The arenga palm (an invasive plant species) hasn't helped the situation, by smothering the vegetation that the rhinos favour and decimating their food supply. Work has begun to eradicate the arenga palm, but it is going to be a long and onerous task.

Illegal poaching and habitat destruction are not the only serious threats to the Javan rhino. The fact the population is so small is a very grave problem, because it can lead to inbreeding and loss of genetic variability. With the shortage of suitable habitat for the Javan rhinos in Ujung Kulon National Park, it is imperative to help find another area to translocate and establish a second population. The plan is to select a group of male and female rhinos of breeding age, to form a "back-up" population in a secure habitat. Unfortunately, the selection process is going to be tough, because these rhinos are extremely difficult to study in the dense tropical forest. It would have been helpful to scientists if they had been kept and bred in captivity, but that has never happened. In fact, only a few people have seen a Javan rhino in the wild. Even people who have been working on the conservation of this rhino for decades have never seen one. Obviously, it is going to be an arduous task to find the appropriate rhinos and translocate them to another safe area, but it has to happen. For the Javan rhino, this is the only insurance plan that conservationists have, lest the Javan rhino become extinct. The species is further threatened by disease, or by the risk of a major volcanic eruption on the island. Hence, their best hope is to establish another population – one under the protection of an armed rhino protection unit.

While it might seem as if there are a number of factors working against the Javan rhino, the future is hopeful. Population biologists estimate that the rhino population could grow to approximately 2500 rhinos in the next 150 years. This is a small figure, yes, and is the minimum requirement for this magnificent species to survive – but there is hope nonetheless.

World's largest "rhino farm"

John Hume is the world's largest and most successful private rhino breeder. Based in South Africa, he firmly believes that captive breeding plans are the way forward to help save rhinos from extinction. He maintains that rhinos can pay for their survival, from their own horns. Hume has about 1,650 white rhinos on his 20,000 acre ranch, equating to 10% of the world's remaining population. He also has a small number of black rhinos. Every rhino on the ranch is dehorned every two to three years. This requires a vet shooting the rhino with a tranquiliser dart. Once the animal has taken the dart and keeled over, the horn is removed painlessly, with an electric saw. In a few years, the horn will have regrown, and the harvesting of the rhino horns can begin again. Hume says the main reason for dehorning is to keep his animals safe from poaching. Critics say he was a businessman before he was a rhino breeder, and by dehorning his rhinos he has amassed more than six tons of rhino horn. Hume's problem is how to sell it legitimately. Rhino horn is worth more than gold or cocaine by weight, so this rhino farmer is sitting on a fortune worth tens of million pounds.

When Hume started his rhino breeding adventure in 2008, it was possible to sell rhino horn legally within South Africa. Hume has always believed that a legal trade in rhino horn will save the rhino from extinction, and is quoted as saying, 'Having taken the horn off, why not sell it? The more horns you sell to Vietnam, the more rhinos in Kruger National Park you will save.' For his business plan to succeed, Hume needed to generate income from selling rhino horn domestically, but more importantly he would benefit by selling his cache of rhino horn to international markets – because the biggest demand for it was in China and Vietnam. Of course, international trade in rhino horn had been banned since 1977, which made things difficult. And it got even worse too, when South Africa put a domestic ban on the sale of rhino horn, in 2009 – after rhino horn started turning up on the black market. The ban lasted until April 2017, when Hume and another rhino breeder were successful in reversing it, after a series of legal challenges in the courts. So, trading in rhino horn on the domestic market within the borders of South Africa was reinstated.

In August 2017, Hume held an online auction to sell 264 rhino horns. Both sellers and buyers had to have a permit in order to trade. Interestingly, the website could translate the English language into Mandarin and Vietnamese, targeting two countries who were the biggest purchasers of rhino horn on the planet. Was he aiming to sell illegally to the international market? The details of the number of lots sold and prices fetched on the auction were never revealed. Afterwards, Hume made it clear that he was disappointed with the lack of interest from buyers, blaming the South African government and adverse publicity. He has not since promoted another auction, after cancelling one originally scheduled for September 2017.

At the beginning of 2019, it was reported that Hume was making an urgent appeal for financial help. Protecting rhinos is a costly business, and he has previously stated that his monthly security bill is about £270,000. Thanks to his complex radar-driven security, he has not lost a rhino to poachers in the last two years, while one rhino is killed every eight hours in South Africa. In 2017, the official number of rhinos killed by poachers in South Africa alone was 1,028. On top of security costs, Hume employs around 100 people to take care of the rhinos on his ranch. Due to recent droughts, there was not enough grass to feed his 1,650 rhinos, and he is now having to buy in dry food to keep his rhinos alive. He has made urgent appeals for potential investors, contributors, and any monetary help, because without more funds his rhinos will die from starvation.

There is no doubt that John Hume cares for the white rhinos on his ranch. He has reportedly invested $100 million of his own money into his rhinos, and insists that his business is about saving rhinos and not making substantial profits. But the key to achieving this is being able to sell rhino horn. Some conservationists agree with Hume, and think that his business plan could indeed have merit. On the other hand, some conservationists don't agree with "farming" rhinos, and feel that the process of breeding and dehorning rhinos on a farm is a long way from their natural existence in the wild, and not palatable. The market for rhino horn seems to be based on traditional medicine and short lived fads. It could take a generation or more for people to give up their beliefs about the importance of rhino horn in traditional medicine. As for rhino horn being a fad – for demonstrating people's social status and wealth – fads can go out of fashion. Unfortunately, rhinos do not have enough time for the people of Southeast Asia to become bored of buying rhino horn, or for these people's children to become educated about the plight of rhinos. It's too late for the next generation to have any impact on the dwindling numbers of one of the most majestic and beautiful animals on this planet – and that's an utter tragedy.

A few last words …

Humankind has failed the elephants and rhinos across the world. We are succeeding in taking their souls and wiping out their physical existence on the planet. There are no more words for this, only tears.

SHELDRICK WILDLIFE TRUST   **Website: www.sheldrickwilfetrust.org**

Tel: 01372 378321   **Registered Charity No 1103836**

"In 2004, The David Sheldrick Wildlife Trust, known as the Sheldrick Wildlife Trust, was established as a registered charity in England & Wales. The UK based charity exists to protect and preserve wildlife and habitats in Kenya through financial contributions, educational outreach and public awareness initiatives."

SAVE THE ASIAN ELEPHANTS   **Website: www.stae.org**

Tel: 0207 841 1186   **Registered Charity No 9834567**

"STAE exerts influence on governments and politician in Europe and Asia and on the tourist industry, to adopt solutions it advances for the welfare of Asian elephants."

INTERNATIONAL RHINO FOUNDATION   **Website: www.rhinos.org**

Email: info@rhinos.org   **NOT FOR PROFIT ORGANISATION**

"Since 1989, the International Rhino Foundation has championed the survival of the world's rhinos through conservation and research. We do what it takes to ensure that rhinos survive for future generations."

SAVE THE RHINO INTERNATIONAL   **Website: www.savetherhino.org**

Email: info@savetherhino.org   **Registered Charity No 1035072**

"We exist to save rhinos and grow the population."

CHAPTER FOUR
Big Cats

"Who will care for the animals, for they cannot look after themselves? Who will raise their voices, when mine is carried away on the wind?"

George Adamson

Plight of the big cats

Big cat populations around the world are on the decline, and they face ongoing threats day after day. In the wild, big cats need a large area to roam, but habitat loss is a problem for all big cats across the planet. Around 80% of the 40 wild cat species in the world are declining in number, and about 16 species are considered vulnerable, endangered, or near threatened. Like most animals in the wild, their numbers are dwindling due to human activity. As the human population has increased, so has deforestation in aid of agriculture, towns, cities, roads, industry, and livestock. Deforestation is particularly affecting tigers in India and jaguars in the Amazon. Loss of habitat has overwhelmingly threatened the survival of the big cats. The tiger has lost a devastating 93% of its natural terrain across Asia, the lion has lost 75% of its territory across Africa, and the jaguar has lost almost 50% of its range in South America.

The top seven big cats are now in trouble, and they need help more than ever before.

Tiger	**Endangered**
Lion	**Vulnerable**
Jaguar	**Near Threatened**
Leopard	**Critically Endangered**
Snow Leopard	**Vulnerable**
Cheetah	**Vulnerable**
Cougar	**Least Concern (population decreasing)**

Hunting and poaching big cats is nothing more than needless killing. They are prized and sought-after for their body parts, simply because people in Southeast Asia believe these body parts have amazing medicinal value – which is certainly not the case. Conflict with people means big cats are hunted and killed because they are a threat to humans, or merely a perceived threat. Their need for large areas to roam leads them to wander outside of the protected areas. Big cats also need an adequate and healthy prey base of deer and other small mammals to survive. Unfortunately, their prey is subject to the same habitat loss, and to hunters. As the big cats' natural prey declines in numbers or is depleted, they will turn to killing livestock on farmland and ranches to survive. Conflict ensues, as farmers kill them to protect their farm and livelihood. The key to helping big cats in the wild is to safeguard their prey. As apex predators, big cats can have a serious impact on ecosystems – controlling prey density by restricting smaller predators. In turn, this can be critical to the conservation of nature. Unfortunately, our planet is increasingly threatened by climate change. Global warming is already having an impact on wildlife, and could be the greatest cause of species extinction in the twenty-first century.

Tiger

The tiger is the largest cat species in the world. Unfortunately, we have lost 97% of the planet's tiger population in the last 100 years. Needless to say, this is a disaster for the future of this magnificent animal. In the wild, the number of tigers has actually risen from a population of around 3,200 in 2010 to almost 4,000 in 2017, but these are only estimates. Of the 9 subspecies of tigers, only six remain, and they are considered critically endangered. These are the Amur (Siberian) tiger, Sumatran tiger, Bengal tiger, Indochinese tiger, Malayan tiger, and South China tiger (which is extinct in the wild). The majority of tigers, around 2000 in number, are found in India. Three subspecies which have recently become extinct, were the Caspian tiger, Javan tiger, and the Bali tiger.

A study in 2004 discovered that there was very little genetic diversity amongst subspecies of tiger, but enough to warrant the division of them. Unfortunately the lack of agreement over the number of these tiger subspecies has frustrated the efforts to recover some from the brink of extinction. The size of a tiger's home territory is dependent on the amount of prey available, and in the case of male tigers, access to female tigers. A female tiger can exist on a territory of say 20 square kilometres, whereas a male's territory is more likely to be 60-100 square kilometres, because his territory will overlap that of several females. Because tigers are indigenous to some of the most densely populated areas on the planet, this has caused discord and hostility with humans.

The Bali tiger has been extinct since 1937 – though there may have been a small number of the species that lasted for another 10 to 20 years. It was physically the smallest tiger subspecies, and lived on the island of Bali near Malaysia and the Philippines. As Bali only had an area of 2,175 square miles, the tiger population could not have been very large. The indigenous settlers of Bali considered tigers to be evil spirits, and thus saw them as a threat. European settlers began to arrive in the late sixteenth century, and for the following 300 years the Bali tiger was hunted to extinction – either for fun, "sport", or for protection from supernatural demons. On the Indonesian island of Java, the Javan tiger was believed to have gone extinct between the 1950s and the 1980s. They were hunted, their habitat was destroyed, and their main prey, rusa deer, were greatly reduced due to disease. There have been sightings of tigers on the island since the 1980s, and more recently in 2016 and 2017 there have been photographs taken of alleged Javan tigers; but this hasn't amounted to a firm conclusion – as experts think the big cats in the photographs could be Javan leopards.

The plains of central Asia, from Turkey through to China, were once home to the giant Caspian tiger – which weighed more than 300 pounds, with some males weighing well over 500 pounds. It roamed thousands of square miles of reed jungles and forests of trees called "tugai" which line the shores of Central Asia's largest rivers. Its prey consisted of wild boar, roe deer, and Bukhara deer. Unfortunately, the Caspian tiger began to lose its habitat to the human population in the nineteenth century, as the "tugai" was turned into agricultural land, and the tiger's prey was hunted and shot. The Caspian tiger was also relentlessly hunted and shot thanks to the Russian government, who put a bounty on the big cat in order to reclaim farmlands adjacent to the Caspian Sea. When Russia withdrew the extermination orders in 1947, the withdrawal came too late to save the Caspian tiger. In the 1970s, the Caspian tiger was officially declared extinct. There has been discussion and work done by scientists to re-introduce the Amur tiger into an area within the previous range of the Caspian tiger. The preserved Caspian tiger's DNA, and the Amur tiger's DNA, are extremely similar; scientists and conservationists are hopeful that the Caspian tiger may once again walk the plains of its ancestors in the coming years. The 6 subspecies of tigers left in the wild today still face a fragile future. In the case of the Amur, Sumatran, and Malayan tigers, their estimated populations are so small – at around 500 – that they are vulnerable to extinction. The Amur has an effective wild population of 35 individuals, because of the genetic diversity of the species. This figure is the lowest ever recorded for a wild population of tigers. And yet, it has been a conservational success, because in the 1940s there were only 20-30 tigers left in the wild. For Sumatran tigers remaining in the wild there have been estimates of 500-600, but their numbers could be as low as 400. Apart from loss of habitat, they are threatened by poachers who illegally sell tiger parts and bones to China. Some tiger products from this subspecies have also found their way into Taiwan, South Korea, and the USA. Malayan tigers are primarily threatened by human activities, as their habitat in the Malaysian rainforest has been converted to support agriculture. With the absence of their normal prey in these areas, the tigers can attack domestic animals, which leads to farmers hunting them down. There has been some conservational effort to protect the Malayan tigers, including anti-poaching efforts, teaching farmers how to better protect their livestock, and removal of snares. But the outcome for the Malayan tiger is still grim.

India is home to the largest population of Bengal tigers, but there are smaller numbers in Bangladesh, Buthan, and Nepal. Bengal tigers are the national animals of both India and Bangladesh. The main threat to their existence is poachers, who kill tigers for body parts to sell, and loss of habitat to human populations – resulting in farmers killing the tigers to protect their livestock. India has been proactive in protecting Bengal tigers, launching the "National Tiger Conservation Authority" or "Project Tiger" in 1973. There are currently about 50 reserves which have the legal status of a national park. Poaching is still a problem, as well as frequent human-tiger issues amongst local people and farmers. But the Indian government does give tigers protection, and the tiger population has increased as a result. In Nepal, new data from 10 years of conservation work has been gathered by the government, showing that their tiger population has almost doubled. Conservationists have estimated there to be 235 tigers living in the country. The challenge going forward is for tiger and human communities to live side by side, sharing the same environment. There is simply no additional land for either of them.

The Indochinese tiger is a small population of tigers across Southern China, Malaysia, Vietnam, Cambodia, Laos, Thailand, and Myanmar. Due to the spread of these tigers across so many countries, it is difficult to determine how many tigers there are. According to researchers' estimates, there are between 750-1,300. About three-quarters of the Indochinese tigers that are killed, end up in Chinese traditional medical concoctions. They are being wiped out faster than any other tiger subspecies. The South China tiger has not been seen in the wild for 25 years. Therefore, it is a functionally extinct animal, because even if there were a few left in the wild they would not have the genetically diverse offspring to regenerate the subspecies. They used to live in the temperate forests of southeast China. Now, there about 100 in Chinese zoos, reserves, and breeding centres.

The most shocking revelation is that there are an estimated 5,000-7,000 tigers being kept in captivity in the USA, according to Born Free USA. Many of these tigers will have been bred by "backyard breeders" and crossbred between subspecies. Many states in the USA have no laws preventing people from keeping exotic pets, and those states that do have laws often don't enforce them. Most of these tigers are off the radar. They are often kept by wealthy people who have some land. There is no registration process, and no regulations for the welfare of these big cats. They are just regarded as luxury items that can be bred, bought, and sold to whoever has the money to pay for them. No doubt many end up in roadside petting zoos, and situations where they are used as entertainment to make profit. The problem is that no one knows how many "pet-tigers" or tigers on breeding farms there are in other countries around the world, as well as in the USA. There are no regulated welfare laws for many of these tigers surviving under private owners. Anecdotal evidence of unwanted tigers being used in canned hunts in the USA is also troubling. Trophy hunters are willing to pay up to $25,000 to shoot a tiger. There is no federal law governing canned hunting operations, nor does the *Animal Welfare Act* regulate game ranches, hunting preserves, or canned hunts in the USA.

Tigers are in crisis in the wild, and we should be angry and concerned about this. A century ago, more than 100,000 tigers lived in the wild across 30 countries. India's increasing tiger population is very encouraging, but it has the support of the Indian government as the national animal of India – the same cannot be said for other countries. The most depressing aspect to the decline of the planet's big cats, is that we are losing so many of them to baseless claims of medicinal value. China could put an end to this catastrophe, because as long as people believe the false claims, our big cats are doomed to extinction.

Lion

Lions are one of the most popular wildlife species on our planet. The idea that this majestic cat may disappear in the wild, in the not too distant future, is unthinkable. A hundred years ago, there were more than 200,000 lions existing in the wild in Africa. According to the IUCN Red List's estimate, there are now currently between 20,000 and 39,000 lions, though a realistic number may be nearer to 20,000. Lions can only be found in parts of eastern and southern Africa. A subspecies can also be found in India's protective Gir National Park – this is the Asiatic lion, which had dropped in numbers to only 10 in the late 1800s. It used to roam across the Middle East and Asia, but they were slaughtered on a grand scale by hunting and killing to protect livestock. Today, numbers have increased to over 500 lions, but this is still a pitifully low number. With villagers living around the Gir National Park patrolling the area for poachers, and conservation groups dedicating their time to this population of lions, human intervention has been a success for this subspecies. However, there are a number of Asiatic lions still in zoos, with no plans to release any into the wild. Meanwhile, there is always the danger that with such a small population living in the wild, the species could be wiped out via a natural disaster or disease.

Like other endangered wildlife species, one of the prime reasons for the decline in the number of lions is loss of habitat. The population of African countries is consistently growing, and requires more land for villages and farming. When farming encroaches on lion territory, there is the problem of lions killing livestock, which can cripple the economy in some areas. When farmers kill lions to stop future attacks on their livestock, lion numbers fall into extensive decline. Existing populations of wild lions in Africa are on the brink of extinction, and their number is drastically smaller than those within better managed and protected national parks. Lions are now extinct in 26 African countries, and have lost 90 per cent of their historic range. In 27 other African countries, small lion populations exist, but only 7 countries have a lion population of more than 1,000. The illegal bushmeat trade is also threatening the lion population in Africa. Traditionally, small rural communities existed on what animals they caught in the wild, with these animals providing their dietary requirement for meat. This would include any non-domestic animals, from apes to bats, crocodiles to antelopes. But today, bushmeat has grown into a large business, requiring millions of tonnes of meat to feed Africa's growing population. The logging industry is hugely responsible for the decline of many wildlife species, because it has unwittingly helped hunters in pursuit of their prey. The industry has built roads helping to carve up primary forest. This has given hunters access to remote and endangered populations of wildlife. Unfortunately, all wildlife is now considered bushmeat, and that includes big game species like lions and even elephants. There is a downside to this for humans too. The meat is not refrigerated, and goes on sale in the local markets where there are no hygiene precautions taken by the "butchers". As such, carcasses are often teeming with flies. This doesn't appear to deter people from buying the meat, as it is cheaper than farmed meat. But bushmeat is known to be a route by which various tropical diseases spread to humans from their animal hosts. Ebola, HIV, smallpox, chicken pox, tuberculosis, and rabies, are just some of the diseases which can be transferred from animals to humans.

Hunting lions in the wild for recreation, for the sake of a trophy, is another unsustainable threat. Traditionally, trophy hunters would track their prey for days and weeks, sometimes for up to a month, and still not kill a lion. Hunters tended to be wealthy Americans, but these days they don't have the time to spend weeks away from their businesses back in the USA. Then canned hunting emerged, which became popular because the kill was quick and 100 per cent guaranteed. There are around 20,000 lions in the wild today, and an estimated further 8,000 captive-bred lions living on the death ranches. Many are bred for particular characteristics that trophy hunters prefer, like black manes or white coats. The captive lion population is growing at a remarkable rate, while numbers of lions in the wild are declining rapidly. Yet the trophy hunting fraternity are adamant that canned hunting takes the pressure off lions in the wild. The truth is that there is no evidence that captive bred lions (who have been inbred for generations) benefit conservation efforts – only the sadistic whims of trophy hunters. There is another fact fuelling the rate of breeding lions in captivity too. During the 1990s, lions were often cheaply bred, with the aim of providing trophy hunters with a quick and guaranteed kill – many of these trophy hunters being American. In 2016, the USA banned the import of all trophies from captive lion hunts in South Africa, because South Africa couldn't demonstrate the conservational value of canned hunting. Very quickly, the number of trophy hunters visiting the canned hunt ranches dropped by half. But another market has opened up, which farmers have quietly been getting ready for – the bone market. This is legal, because the South African government has issued permits, allowing farmers on these canned hunting ranches to export lion skeletons to wildlife product dealers in Asia. The money is good. The dealers in Asia then resell the lion skeletons on as "tiger bone" to the traditional medicine market. Again and again, we are told that there is no scientific proof that tiger or lion bones have any medicinal benefits, but wildlife is still being slaughtered to extinction, at no benefit or purpose to man or beast.

Sadly, the canned hunting industry and the South African government appear to want to encourage captive lion breeding. The reason being is that they see canned hunting as a way of sustainable utilisation of natural resources. They also consider it as part of the "green economy" where the aim is to provide "sustainable development without degrading the environment". The South African government don't appear to be bothered by the way the canned hunting industry is exploiting wild animals for personal greed, or by the lack of morals and ethics surrounding the practice.

Asian wildlife dealers are powerful syndicates, who finance wildlife crime in many countries across the world. Between 2008 and 2016, South Africa exported more than 6,000 lion skeletons, with a total weight of more than 70 tonnes, to Southeast Asian countries. These exports still continue. Asian wildlife syndicates see lion bones as a useful substitute for tiger bones – for which there are well established markets. Tigers have been listed on CITES Endangered Species treaty, meaning all international trade in their parts is banned. So, importing lion bones and then passing them off as tiger bones is useful. In China, bones are used to make "tiger-bone wine", by suspending big cat skeletons in large vats of alcohol. In Vietnam, lion bones are made into "tiger-bone cake". This is made by boiling bones with turtle shell and other items, until the bones and shell disintegrate. The liquid is then compacted in a chocolate, bar-like cake. The wildlife syndicates are always dreaming up new products to sell at extortionate prices. One example in the tiger goods market, is bones with reddish smudges which they call "pink bone". Buyers are told that the colour in the bone comes from de-boning the tiger while it is still alive, because it leaves blood in the bone and has medicinal value.

It is hugely ironic for farmers in South Africa to claim that they are providing a sustainable substitute for the tiger bone market, when there has been a sharp increase in the rampant poaching of wild lions in countries around South Africa and captive lions within South Africa. This is not sustainable – because we're losing all our beautiful lions. And it's even more ironic, because only the heads and feet are being removed. These are then taken to be used for trinket jewellery in Asian markets. In 2018, South Africa announced that it was doubling the annual export quota of lion skeletons from 800 to 1500, thereby encouraging more trafficking of African lion bones, which could increase the demand and give the trafficking an air of legitimacy.

The South African government maintains that by increasing the skeleton quota it will "draw down growing stockpiles of lion bones at captive facilities". They also firmly believe that if captive breeding facilities are restricted, then dealers will seek further supplies by poaching captive-bred and wild lions. This is something that is already happening, and suggests that dealers and farmers are more concerned about making a profit, to the detriment of the planet's iconic wild lions.

Jaguar

The only predator the jaguar appears to have, is humans. They are the third largest cat in the world, with powerful jaws and a dominant nature. Physically, the jaguar most closely resembles a leopard, but it has a more substantial build and its behavioural characteristics are closer to those of a tiger. Jaguars live alone outside of the mating season, and will fiercely protect their territory. They eat deer, peccaries, tapirs, alligators, monkeys, snakes, turtles, sloths, eggs, fish, and anything else they can catch. Jaguars are very adept at climbing trees, though they tend to hunt on the ground. They are also strong swimmers, like tigers.

The WWF estimates that there are only about 15,000 jaguars still living in the wild. But this estimate is difficult to verify due to the jaguar's elusive existence. This fascinating carnivore used to be found throughout South America and North America. Today, they are rarely seen in North America, though there have been rare sightings in Arizona, Texas, and New Mexico. They are protected, which has stopped the shooting of this endangered species for its pelt. In South America, jaguars tend to be restricted to remote areas of rainforest and swamps, usually around the humid Amazon basin. The hunting of jaguars is banned in many South American countries, though countries like Brazil, Costa Rica, Guatemala, Mexico, and Peru allow hunting of "problem animals".

So, what are the dangers to this near threatened species? Firstly, destruction of their natural forest habitat from logging and mining is pushing the jaguar to extinction. Jaguars are also under threat from farmers, who see them attacking and taking their livestock. But the greatest threat, which is decimating their numbers, is the appalling international trafficking of jaguar body parts for jewellery and medicinal "glue". World Animal Protection (WAP) has been investigating these secretive networks of hunters, smugglers, and organised crime gangs, and the multi-million pound trafficking routes they weave. You won't be surprised to learn that the majority of these routes lead to China. Many of the imported jaguar body parts come from a country called Suriname. Suriname is a country located on the northern coast of South America, sandwiched between Guyana and French Guiana. The south of the country is covered with pristine tropical rainforests. There is no reliable estimate of how many jaguars exist in these rainforests, but well over a hundred are killed for their body parts every year. A number of charities including WWF, WAP, and International Fund for Animal Welfare (IFAW) have carried out investigations regarding the trafficking of jaguar parts. China is the main destination for these products. Some 20 years ago, a wave of Chinese migrants entered Suriname as miners, loggers, and shop owners. It wasn't long before they were running major mining, logging, road, and building projects, due to concessions in the interior jungle. As the Chinese migrant population expanded, and their prosperity increased, the market for jaguar parts began to grow rapidly. The Chinese call the jaguars "American tigers", therefore linking them by name with the products from tigers which have been popular in traditional Asian medicine for over 1,000 years.

Jaguars are caught by hunters, who stalk the big cats based on a bounty or a kill-to-order request. It can take days to find a jaguar, and hours to stalk and kill after the first shot has been fired and only wounded the big cat. The jaguars are often shot numerous times before they are eventually killed, which means the poor creature suffers an agonising and painful death. In Suriname, killing, transporting, buying, or selling a protected species is against the law, and is punishable by a huge fine and years in jail.

But the networks put in place by traffickers allow the dead animal to reach the capital – Paramaribo – without detection. Here, the jaguar carcass will be taken to a Chinese owned shop, where it is unlikely to be investigated by police, because the Chinese in Suriname run all the shops and exert a lot of influence in the community.

Once the carcass arrives at the shop, it is boiled down over a period of up to a week, until it turns into a dark, paste-like substance. This is then put into a small tub; these tubs can be smuggled back to China, via hand luggage. Tiger balm ointment is often put in the same hand luggage, because it has a strong smell and can confuse airport sniffer dogs. As so many people go back and forth to China, selling the jaguar paste is a good way to earn some extra money – selling it to family and friends on each visit. Tubs of jaguar paste can sell for up to $3000, and as many as 20 to 30 tubs can be made from one single jaguar carcass. Jaguar teeth are passed off for tiger teeth in China. The teeth and claws are made into necklaces and other jewellery. They are then worn as status symbols of wealth and importance. They may be worn in the belief that they can protect the wearer from evil. Sometimes jaguar cubs are taken from the wild when a female adult has been killed, and these cubs can find their way into the illegal pet trade – ultimately they end up being purchased by wealthy business people, who like to keep them as status symbols.

Leopard

Leopards are the smallest of the big cats, with long, lithe bodies, sturdy legs, and large paws. They are very powerful animals and are notorious for dragging their prey up into trees even when said prey is much heavier than themselves. Leopards are found throughout most of Africa, and across parts of Asia, from the Middle East to Korea, China, India, and Malaysia. They live in a variety of habitats, including forests, mountains, grassland, and deserts. There are no reliable estimates of populations, due to the elusiveness of leopards and the huge areas they haunt. But it is thought that there are over 100,000 in Africa and fewer than 10,000 in Asia. With the decline in numbers, leopards are now considered rare in most of West Africa. There are 9 subspecies of leopards: the African leopard, Sri Lankan leopard, Javan leopard, Indochinese leopard, Amur leopard, North-Chinese leopard, Persian leopard, Arabian leopard, and Indian leopard. The species as a whole is on the decline, and some researchers think they are on the path to extinction.

African leopards are native to more than 35 African countries. Their habitats are diverse, from deserts to savanna grasslands, mountainous regions to rainforests. They are also known to survive in urban and suburban areas populated with people. Unfortunately, leopard populations adjacent to human settlements are becoming depleted, as these animals are hunted for bushmeat. Trophy hunting is also having a negative effect on the number of leopards, despite trophy hunters parading as conservationists and purportedly only killing the old and weak animals. Leopards outside of protected areas are being driven towards extinction, as their historical ranges are disappearing due to habitat loss and excessive fragmentation.

Sri Lanka is home to the biggest leopard in the world, known as the Sri Lankan leopard. This native subspecies was first defined in 1956 by a Sri Lankan zoologist. By 2008 the Sri Lankan leopard was listed as endangered on the IUCN Red List. The relatively undisturbed rain forests of the central highlands of Sri Lanka have the highest density of leopards in the wild. Once, these leopards were found in all areas across Sri Lanka, but they are now found mainly in protected areas – which play a significant role in keeping these top predators, who are so important to the ecosystem of the island, safe from poachers.

There have been 30 years of civil unrest in Sri Lanka, which only came to an end in 2009. The strenuous task of removing many war mines had to be achieved before vital conservation efforts could be put in place. But people returning from war, to former areas, have been reclaiming land. This is putting the leopards' protected areas under threat. Hunting is another significant threat – for the leopard's coveted skin – and hunters will often lay out wire traps to catch unsuspecting leopards. The government of Sri Lanka has a "Leopard Project" in place, to ensure the conservation of the leopards. This project is implemented in coordination with other wildlife charities. The estimates given for leopards in the wild are over 600 in the protected areas, and around 160 outside the protected areas. Certainly, the total number of leopards is understood to not exceed 1,000, with a sub-population of no more than 250.

The Indonesian island of Java is home to the Javan leopard, which is listed on the IUCN Red List as critically endangered. There has been little research on the Javan leopard, and there is very little data on the estimated population of Javan leopards left in the wild. There could be less than 250 adults, and a decreasing population trend is worrying; it is the last big cat left in Indonesia, after the Javan tiger became extinct on the island in the 1980s. Half of Indonesia's human population lives on Java, and with so much habitat loss, depletion of prey, and illegal hunting, the Javan leopard is being pushed to extinction. The national parks are the best protected habitat for Javan leopards, but an estimated half of the leopard population is living in unprotected areas.

The Indochinese leopard can be found on the mainland in Southeast Asia and southern China. Their numbers appear to be declining at a rapid rate, and the Indochinese leopard is struggling for survival. It can only be found in about 6 per cent of its previous historical range. The major threat to the Indochinese leopard is illegal poaching, because (like lions) leopards are being used as a substitute for tiger body parts – as genuine tiger parts become scarce. In the wild, there are an estimated 970-2500 Indochinese leopards left, and researchers have recommended an urgent IUCN assessment for the Indochinese leopard, and that it be classified as endangered.

With less than 100 Amur leopard adults in the wild, they are one of the world's most endangered big cats. Driven to the edge of extinction, the Amur leopard has made a credible recovery, though they are not out of danger yet. This subspecies is a nocturnal animal that lives and hunts alone in the vast forests of Russia and China. They have long been subjected to poaching and being shot by trophy hunters for their beautiful, thick spotted fur pelts. They have also been killed because subsistence hunters don't want them killing the sika deer and other prey, and farmers will kill them to protect their livestock.

North Chinese leopards are endemic to China, and can be found mainly in the Taihang Mountains, with sparse numbers populating five other provinces. This species has been upgraded to vulnerable on the IUCN Red List. Due to lack of research, there are no reliable estimates of the population of North Chinese leopards in the wild. In 2015, *The International Journal of Conservation* suggested that there were up to 350 North Chinese leopards in the wild. Meanwhile, there have been significant attacks on livestock. Locals tend to be Tibetan people who have a Buddhism-based benevolent culture, and therefore have not carried out retaliatory attacks on the leopards. The local government has been paying out compensation to the locals for their animals, but no one knows how long they will continue to do so.

Persian leopards, also known as Caucasian leopards, are on the IUCN Red List too – they are classified as endangered. They can be found across Iran, Armenia, Turkmenistan, Afghanistan, and Georgia. Living in remote mountainous areas, they still face a variety of threats to their existence. These include loss of habitat, reduction of prey species through poaching, encounters with livestock owners, the building of highways, expanding villages, being hunted as trophies for their fur, and a heavy military presence in their area. A population estimate of 550-850 leopards for Iran has been put forward, but there are no estimates from the other countries where Persian leopards have been seen.

Arabian leopards have lost over 98 per cent of their historical range, and are now only found in the Dhofar mountains, in the south eastern part of the Arabian peninsula. The government has taken measures to conserve leopards in Oman, and they are now protected by royal decree. On the IUCN Red List, Arabian leopards are classified as critically endangered, with less than 200 of them in the wild. The Indian leopard population was estimated to be around 12,000-14,000 leopards in a 2015 census. This has increased from a low of 6000-7000 in the 1960s. Like all wildlife in India, leopards are protected, so less than 100 leopards are killed each year. On the other hand, almost 1000 people are injured by leopards every year. The leopard exists in small fragmented populations across India. Due to them being elusive and essentially nocturnal, they are creatures who are difficult to study in the wild.

Snow leopard

Nobody knows how many snow leopards are left in the wild. They have a vast habitat range of more than two million square kilometres across the snowy highlands and mountains of Central Asia. In these areas, where they are thinly spread, they can be difficult to find and study. They mostly reside in the mountainous regions of Russia, Kazakhstan, Bhutan, Tajikistan, Mongolia, Uzbekistan, India, Afghanistan, Nepal, Pakistan, and China. Snow leopards are elusive creatures, which is why they are referred to as the "ghosts of the mountains". Residing in the Himalayas, at extreme altitude and in bitterly cold temperatures, who knows how many of these big cats are living in the wild today? There are some estimates of only 4,000, and other estimates that are around the 8,000 mark. In the last two decades, snow leopards were suspected of declining by at least 20 per cent. They were classified as endangered on the IUCN Red List, but were reclassified as vulnerable in 2017 – based on an estimate of 8,000. Snow leopards are solitary creatures, and they are very successful predators. Mountain sheep and goats are their preferred prey. By keeping the numbers of herbivores down, the meagre alpine plants are not overgrazed, thus leaving some food for grazing for other animals. The snow leopard's spotted coat is thick enough to insulate it from extreme cold, and its feet are covered in fur, allowing them to be used like natural snowshoes. The snow leopard's tail is long and thick, and is used for balance when walking along steep and narrow ledges. It can also be used to keep the snow leopard warm.

The number of threats to snow leopards appear to be increasing. Even in a location as wild and remote as the Himalayan Mountains, they are experiencing habitat loss and fragmentation of their environment, as humans encroach. Poaching is becoming more and more common. In 2016, a report found that 450 snow leopards are poached annually, mainly for body parts for traditional Chinese medicine and trophy skins. Climate change is becoming problematic, as glaciers melt and overgrazing from livestock speeds up mountain erosion, slowing down plants' ability to regenerate.

Reports of snow leopards killing or attacking humans are unheard of, and they are renowned for avoiding human contact if they can. More than 50 per cent of humans living in the snow leopards' range are involved in farming and herding. Many of them are living in poverty. So, when snow leopards kill livestock, the owners of said livestock are keen to retaliate. Panthera are committed to helping snow leopards, as they research and count them, and that includes helping local farmers in return for them not killing the snow leopards. At the same time, snow leopards are attracting both tourists and scientists. Local herders and farmers are turning their homes into hotels and guest houses. Villagers are being employed as snow leopard spotters, and take part in organised treks. The snow leopards are putting money into the pockets of the local community. This is probably the best chance to help the snow leopards' long term survival – humans and wildlife living side by side, for the benefit of both.

Cheetah

Cheetahs are the most unique member of the cat family. They have amazing powers of acceleration, and can go from 0 to 60 miles an hour in only 3 seconds. Their long tail acts as a rudder, helping them to turn corners at high speed. They have incredible eyesight and semi-retractable claws that act as a pair of running spikes, and provide grip when chasing their prey. Unfortunately, the reality is that the world's fastest land mammal has declined so heavily in number that conservationists and environmental scientists are calling for the IUCN Red List to move the species from vulnerable to endangered. In other words, the cheetah is seriously "racing" towards extinction.

There are five subspecies of cheetah. In Africa, there is the Northwest African cheetah, the South African cheetah, the Sudanese cheetah, and the Tanzanian cheetah, and three of them are classified as vulnerable, though the numbers are still declining. The Northwest African cheetah has been classified on the IUCN Red List as critically endangered, with less than 250 adults in the wild. The Asiatic cheetah is also critically endangered. It is almost extinct in Asia, apart from one isolated pocket in Iran, with less than 50 individual adult cheetahs. In 2016, researchers estimated that there were 7,100 cheetahs left on the planet. Cheetahs once roamed almost all of Africa and a large part of Asia. Today, the species is confined mainly to only six African countries. In the last 100 years, cheetahs have been driven out of 91 per cent of their historic domain. Of those 7,100 wild cheetahs left in the world today, only 21 per cent of their range is protected. Cheetahs need vast areas to roam, and can cross areas in excess of 1,000 square kilometres every year. They cannot all be put in protected areas, because the density of cheetahs in those areas is already at the maximum. The challenge is finding land on a larger scale, and implementing regional strategies and national action plans in order to help the long-term conservation of the cheetah. Cheetahs are not a danger to humans, but humans are a danger to them. There are no records of cheetahs killing human beings. Like all the other big cats, the major threat to cheetahs is loss of habitat and fragmentation of small habitat areas. Ranchers and farmers often kill cheetahs because it is perceived that the big cats will be a danger to their livestock. The illegal bushmeat trade, setting snares, is another problem. Cheetahs are vulnerable, and often get fatally caught up in such traps. Larger predators like lions on savanna grasslands can cause problems too. They don't kill adult cheetahs, but they will eat cheetah cubs, causing juvenile mortality in cheetahs to reach as high as 95%. Hence, cheetah mothers will move their cubs to different locations every few days to try and hide them from any lions in the area.

Unfortunately, there is big concern over the illegal trade of cheetah cubs for pets from North Africa. Many are destined for the Gulf States in the Middle East, but they can be sent to other parts of the world too. Owning a cheetah appears to be the latest fad for wealthy Instagrammers in the Gulf States. They use social media to show off their photos and videos of their pet cheetahs playing and hunting. On YouTube there are videos of pet cheetahs hunting and catching gazelles. There are also numerous video tutorials, providing advice on how to tame and train these wild animals to be domestic pets. Thousands of cheetah cubs have likely been trafficked out of Africa during the last ten years. According to the Cheetah Conservation Fund, 1,367 cheetahs were offered for sale on the internet between February 2012 and July 2018, mostly on Instagram for large amounts of money. For every one that is bought, 4 or 5 will die on the journey. Disturbing statistics, to say the least. Young cheetahs can fetch up to $10,000 on the black market. Baby cubs of just a few weeks old fetch the highest prices, with females being more expensive, because they tend to hunt better than males. In the wild, farmers can find and capture cheetah cubs. Selling one cub for a few hundred US dollars can feed a family for months. Laws are very lenient, and the farmer is not likely to be tried and sent to prison for their actions. Trafficking cheetah cubs from the wild and sending them across the world to be sold as pets, has got to be one of the most grotesque travesties inflicted on this stunning species. It's especially egregious when you consider that cheetahs could be facing extinction in the not too distant future.

Cougar

There are six or seven subspecies of cougar across 28 countries in the Americas. They all have different names, but they are essentially the same animal. They can be found in southern areas of Alaska, all the way down to the southern end of Chile. Generally, in North America, they are called cougars, whilst in South America they are known as pumas. They can also be referred to as Florida panthers, mountain lions, or catamounts, and are known collectively as "Puma concolor". Recent tests have proven that these differently named big cats are genetically the same. Like many of the big cats, cougars are mainly solitary. They stalk and ambush their prey. They need dense vegetation or cover to hide from their prey whilst they are hunting. When they get close enough to their prey, the cougar will pounce, usually going for the jugular. Since 1890 there have been less than 100 attacks reported on humans, causing approximately 20 fatalities. It is rare to encounter a cougar, hence attacks by a cougar only happen under exceptional circumstances. There are an estimated 30,000 cougars in the western United States. Cougars were once widely distributed in the western hemisphere, but have been forced out of two-thirds of the areas they occupied. In North America, the cougar can be found in most western states and some western Canadian provinces. Texas has a viable population of cougars, which are seen as "nuisance wildlife". This means that anyone holding a hunting or trapping permit can kill a cougar, regardless of the season, the sex of the animal, or its age.

Since it has now been approximately 80 years since the eastern cougar was last seen, it has been declared by the US conservation authorities as officially extinct. For the last 43 years, the eastern cougar has been on the list of endangered and threatened species. The last confirmed sighting of an eastern cougar was in 1938 – when said animal was killed by a hunter. It is likely that the reason for their demise was due to the influx of European immigrants in the nineteenth century, who killed the cougars to protect themselves and their farm livestock. At the same time, much of the cougars' habitat disappeared through deforestation, to clear trees for farmland. In turn, this forced the cougars' main source of prey, the white-tailed deer, to the brink of extinction in the area. Cougars have been declared extinct in North Carolina, but people still come forward now and then to say that they've spotted cougars in the area. In Florida, the estimated number of Florida panthers is fewer than 200, and this represents the only known breeding population on the eastern side of North America. By 1967, the Florida panther was listed as an endangered subspecies by the Department of the Interior. The US Fish & Wildlife Service has worked closely with the State of Florida and other federal services and charitable organisations to help the recovery of the Florida panther. A genetic restoration plan was implemented in 1995, with the release of 8 female pumas from Texas into the territory of the Florida panther. They are the closest remaining puma population to the Florida panther. Out of the original 8 pumas, 5 produced 20 cubs. None of the 8 pumas from Texas are still remaining in the wild today. Five died from various causes, and the remaining 3 were put into captivity.

In 2008, it was determined that when the Florida panther was established with 3 populations of at least 240 adults, and habitat to support these populations was acquired, then the Florida panther would be taken off the endangered list. It would be great to think that the Florida panther is a success story, when numbers have recovered from about 30 in the 1990s to approximately 200 panthers today. But that would be foolish, especially when every year dozens of Florida panthers are hit and killed by vehicles. There are also many conservational challenges to overcome. The urban sprawl of heavily populated Florida continues to grow, with residential developments, road construction, reclaimed land for agriculture, and mining operations. There is a large development proposed as a major project for the State, of up to 45,000 acres of rural Collier county in south-west Florida. This was proposed by a coalition of 11 major Florida landowners, and the plan is for housing and commercial development as well as new sand and gravel mines. Several new cities would be created, with thousands of new residents, their cars, and hundreds of miles of new roads. The Fish & Wildlife Service say the preservation of the Florida panthers' hunting and roaming area is key to the survival of these panthers in the wild – and that area includes 20,000 acres of the Colliery development. Under the *Endangered Species Act*, government approval is required for this significant development. With the current president, this may not be a favourable judgement for the Florida panther.

In South America, the puma population is mainly unknown, but they are suspected to be on the decline. Pumas are legally protected in 17 out of the 21 countries they populate. Yet they are still killed in many protected countries because of their depredation of livestock. In Brazil, it is permitted to kill pumas to protect livestock. The conservation status of pumas in most South American countries is somewhat unknown. Pumas are considered vulnerable in the northeast and southeast of Brazil. In Costa Rica, pumas are considered endangered. In Mexico, the puma's status varies across each state. The most critical factor affecting pumas in nearly all the South American countries, is the loss and fragmentation of habitat. Rapid human population growth means that some of the poorest people have to encroach on rural areas to live and feed themselves. Subsistence hunting is a major problem, especially when the prey favoured by subsistence hunters coincides with pumas. There is an impact on the puma population, because a reduction of the prey base affects the survival of these animals. There is simply not enough food to go around. Pumas will soon be forced to live out in the extreme environments of high mountain ranges, deserts, and humid wastelands. Even without information on puma populations across most of the South American countries, the inevitable human population growth will cause the puma to go into decline.

A few last words ...

Protecting and conserving big cats in the world today is not straightforward. The biggest problem is humans, who have taken part in the destruction of the habitats of these wild creatures. This leads to reduced biodiversity and weakened ecosystems, which will in due course be a major threat to human existence too. The future demands that humans value the existence of our wildlife, and guarantee that wildlife has an expanse of habitat in which to live their natural lives.

PANTHERA USA   Website: www.panthera.org

Email: info@panthera.org   Not For Profit Organisation

"Panthera's mission is to ensure a future for wild cats and the vast landscapes on which they depend. Our vision is a world where wild cats thrive in healthy, natural and developed landscapes that sustain people and biodiversity."

BORN FREE FOUNDATION   Website: www.bornfree.org.uk

Email: info@bornfree.org.uk   Registered Charity No. 1070906

"Since 1984, we have been working tirelessly to ensure that all wild animals, whether living in captivity or in the wild, are treated with compassion and respect. We work across the world to preserve and protect wildlife in its natural habitat – finding Compassionate Conservation solutions so that humans and wildlife can co-exist peacefully."

WORLD ANIMAL PROTECTION   Website: www.worldanimalprotection.org.uk

Email: reception@worldanimalprotection.org   Registered Charity No. 1081849

"We are World Animal Protection:

We end the needless suffering of animals.

We influence decision makers to put animals on the global agenda.

We help the world see how important animals are to all of us.

We inspire people to change animals' lives for the better.

We move the world to protect animals."

CHAPTER FIVE
Dolphins and Whales

"It is a dolphin's birth right to swim in a straight line in the ocean as far as its heart desires."

Ric O Barry

Why do we love whales and dolphins?

Watching whales and dolphins swimming in the sea, free and wild in their natural environment, provides truly special moments and unforgettable memories. It's stunning to see these fabulous marine animals doing spectacular acrobatic movements, playing, and having fun. They look happy and free, and we all confess our love for them. It's amazing to know that there are as many as 90 species of whales, dolphins, and porpoises in the world. There are blue whales living in every ocean on the planet, and they are the largest mammal that has ever lived. But we know so little about them. We know hardly anything about their mating habits, their social lives, their movements, how far they travel, and so on. How about sperm whales, with the largest brain, the largest head, and the loudest sound of any mammal on our planet? What about the orcas, also known as killer whales, who are actually the largest member of the dolphin family? In the dolphin family, we have over 40 species of dolphin, all unique in their identity and characteristics, spread across the planet in all oceans and several large rivers. So many wonderful whales and dolphins ... wouldn't it be fantastic if we could ensure they would be around forever?

When we talk to people about whales and dolphins, the vast majority will say they love them. Some people believe they have a warm affinity with whales and dolphins. Scientists have documented that wild dolphins in certain species have sought out social encounters with humans. These marine mammals like to be inquisitive, and it's this behaviour that supports the idea that dolphins like to seek out human contact. Being clearly intelligent, and on the whole placid, is perhaps what gives us a feeling that we can bond with them. The fact that dolphins live and travel in social and family groups, caring for their young and foraging for food, is also a big plus for us humans. It's a pattern of kinship that we can all relate to and accept. But of course, there are many unanswered questions too. From day to day, how do dolphins live? Why do they have to go to particular places to breed each year? How are they able to communicate across such long distances? There is so much we don't know about dolphins, that we tend to think of them as magical, or otherworldly. The sound of dolphin and whale calls are popular, and are often used in meditation and relaxation videos and music DVDs. Their smooth and playful movements under the sea make us feel relaxed and at peace. There's nothing quite like watching whales and dolphins on video, gliding through pristine blue water with calm and ease, at the same time communicating with each other. In essence, they give a sense of harmony or inner peace to those of us who watch and listen – something many of us crave in our daily lives. We have anecdotes and stories over thousands of years where dolphins have interacted with humans. This has often been interpreted as dolphins saving humans from the dangers of the sea. There are many occurrences of dolphins "saving" shipwrecked humans, divers, and surfers from sharks. Occasionally, it may be one dolphin coming to the rescue, but sometimes whole groups or family pods have appeared to help humans. Some humans have been lifted to the surface of the sea by dolphins, to help them survive. Dolphins have been known to form a tight, protective circle around humans when sharks are drawing in. We do not have specific explanations as to why these amiable creatures have helped humans, but there are quite a few theories. Dolphins are very protective of their young calves, and are defensive when they know predators are around. Perhaps they are picking up on the distress of humans and are willing to come to their aid. A dolphin's sonar can penetrate a human body, allowing them to see our skeletons, lungs, and hearts. They could be picking up a fast heart rate, and are familiar with the signs of stress and helplessness. They also have a readiness to help beached whales in shallow waters, and even play with them out in the oceans.

But, let's not get carried away thinking that these wild marine mammals yearn to be friends with humans. Of the 40 or so species of dolphins, the only contact they have probably had with humans is riding the bow waves of their ships and boats, or when they get caught in fishing nets. Any recorded friendly encounters between dolphins and humans tend to be with bottlenose dolphins or spotted dolphins. Why would wild dolphins take a shine to humans and want to be friends with them? It's a fact that dolphins, particularly lone, unsociable dolphins, have been known to act aggressively, and have attempted to injure humans. So, let's play down their over-friendliness, and see them for what they are – wild and free and living in complex social groups in the oceans. We can still admire them and watch them leap and frolic from a distance, knowing they are breathtaking and awesome creatures. They have a place in the ecosystem of our planet, and they merit our protection.

Which is the smartest species on the planet?

Why do humans believe they are the smartest species on the planet? If we were, then there's every chance the planet wouldn't be in the mess it's in now. But humans mistakenly think that because animals don't think or communicate like us, they are not as intelligent as us. Scientists have long known that cetaceans (all whales, dolphins, and porpoises) have an incredible ability to feel emotions, understand complex problems, and communicate in ways we cannot even imagine – but still some humans cannot subscribe to this. Whales have the biggest brains of any of the animals on our planet. Does that mean whales are the most intelligent? Studies have tended to relate to bottlenose dolphins, because they are so inquisitive and relatively easy to study in captivity. Whales are more difficult to assess, due to their size and the fact they live far out in the ocean most of the time.

Orcas have been caught and kept in captivity over the years, and over the last three to four decades an increasing number have actually been bred in captivity. Orcas have the second largest brain amongst all the cetaceans in the world. Their brain can weigh as much as 15 pounds, and scientists have discovered that they are particularly intelligent. In the wild, there has been no evidence of an orca killing humans. There have been some injuries to humans, but marine biologists believe these attacks are likely down to mistaken identity. On the other hand, researchers are not surprised that an orca kept in a tank for years, away from other orcas, could have a fatal encounter with a human. Tilikum, the killer whale featured in the documentary "Blackfish", drew international attention after dragging a SeaWorld trainer to her death during a show in 2010 at Orlando, SeaWorld. He had already killed two other humans whilst in captivity. Tilikum spent over 30 years living in extremely confined enclosures, day after day, week after week, year after year. Some of the tanks he spent time in were only about twice his body length – enough to drive him insane. In the wild, orcas live in large social groups. They should not be kept in isolation, cut off from other orcas, in such confined inhumane circumstances. It is no wonder they lose their minds. They eventually become ill and die, when they should be swimming in their vast, natural ocean environment. The problem of measuring the level of intelligence of whales and dolphins is that, as humans, we are doing this from a human perception of what intelligence is. Different species have different skill sets, which can depend on their environment or their physical make up. For example, the sonar of a dolphin is far superior to the man-made sonar that humans use in underwater communication and in position-finding devices. Cetaceans' primary sense is the same as their primary sense of communication, and both are auditory. Communication amongst cetaceans is so strong that scientists believe they can project an "auditory image" that replicates a sonar message they receive. They can literally convey images to others of their species, by sending them an image of a fish or another object under the water. They are also capable of receiving 20 times the amount of information as humans can, with their hearing ability.

Pilot whales have twice as many neurons in their cerebral cortex as humans. They display an intelligence similar to bottlenose dolphins, and are equally as trainable for learning tricks and displays in a dolphinarium, or retrieving items from the ocean floor. Historically, they have had low survival rates in captivity. In their natural environment, they live in complex social structures, in pods numbering 100 or more – so it goes without saying that an isolated life, in a small tank, is nothing short of hell for these magnificent creatures.

Spindle neurons have been located in the brains of various whales and dolphins. Scientists have discovered larger neurons called spindle or "von Economo neurons" which appear to play a central role in the development of intelligence. They can be described as specialised brain cells associated with the ability to "recognise, remember, reason, communicate, perceive, adapt to change, problem solve and understand." This suggests that these cetaceans do a lot more thinking than previously thought. Dolphins have been able to recognise themselves in mirrors and solve problems. They are also able to correlate a part of their own anatomy with that of a human's. For example, when a human trainer waves his arm, a dolphin will wave his fin. Research has shown that dolphins can even create personalised whistles for individual members in a pod, therefore making it easier to communicate when swimming across the oceans. Until recently, scientists thought that spindle neurons were only found in human and primate brains. They have now discovered them not only in some species of cetaceans, but also in the brains of African and Asian elephants – who are also socially complex.

With all this intelligence, it goes without saying that the tricks and sign language taught to dolphins and whales in captivity, are nothing short of a mockery – especially when they depend on these simple feats to get fed. If the animals don't do what is required, they don't eat. Their meals are earnt through doing what they are told to do. Dolphins and whales can solve problems on their own, use gadgets and tools, display joy and grief, and they can participate in complicated large social groups in their natural environment – and yet we're using them for party tricks.

Is the International Whaling Commission fit for purpose?

The International Whaling Commission (IWC) was set up in 1946. Its purpose was "to provide for the proper conservation of whale stocks and thus make possible the orderly development of the whaling industry". Unfortunately, this purpose has been absent in the IWC for decades – something which is made even more evident by claims of corruption, malpractice, and secrecy amongst the member countries supporting the IWC. Currently there are about 89 member countries, and each country has a single vote, regardless of its population size, its economic capacity, or whether or not it has an interest in the whaling industry. The IWC has not achieved conservation and protection for cetacean species across the globe. The whaling industry made a mockery of the global moratorium on whaling in the 1980s, thanks to Japan. Some years later, Norway and Iceland followed in Japan's footsteps, by recommencing commercial whaling – and have continued to do so ever since. It appears there is no jurisdiction from the IWC to stop countries continuing in the commercial industry of killing whales. If a country wants to start commercial whaling again, it only requires a permit from their government to carry it out. Only member EU countries have to abide by the Economic Union's laws, which state: *"All whale species and other cetaceans are protected from deliberate disturbance, capture or killing within EU waters. The EU legislation prohibits the keeping, transport and sale or exchange, of specimens taken from the wild and bans the introduction of cetaceans into the Union for primarily commercial purposes."*

Unfortunately, cetaceans can migrate across the globe, so they can swim in and out of EU waters. Once outside, there is no protection for these marine mammals from the EU. But the real problem is in effect the IWC – it has so little authority that it makes the group look useless, ineffectual, and feeble. In the words of Paul Watson, founder and CEO of Sea Shepherd, 'The IWC no longer has any credibility, it is an irrelevant organisation. Many of the nations voting for Japan have zero interest in the issue of whaling. They vote the way they are paid to vote.' Within the IWC, the members are either pro-whaling countries or anti-whaling countries. Both sides have been keen to persuade as many member countries as they can to support their side. The anti-whaling countries have used their diplomatic strength to persuade countries to side with them. Japan has always been notoriously active in persuading or bribing countries to join the IWC and pledge their votes to support pro-whaling Japan. They have paid member countries' joining fees, delegates' hotel fees, travel, and other expenses, and of course they have provided foreign aid to help small countries. Interestingly, a reasonable number of European countries with no coastlines or connections to the whaling industry have pledged their support to Japan. Basically, Japan buys the votes required for them to manipulate the IWC and get what they want. Denmark is pro-whaling because it upholds the whaling interests of the Faroe Islands, even though the EU does not allow EU countries and their citizens to kill cetaceans. This is despite the fact that around 80% of the Faroese hold Danish passports. Holding a passport "certifies the identity and nationality of its holder", so does that mean the majority of people living in the Faroe Islands are Danish citizens? If so, why are they allowed to slaughter up to nearly 2,000 pilot whales a year?

When the whaling ban came into effect in 1986, Japan continued to hunt and kill whales. Their commercial whaling operations became Japan's scientific whaling programme. What was the difference between the two activities? Apparently nothing, and Japan's veil of "scientific research" has never produced any data published by reputable scientific journals. Many of Japan's "research" objectives are flawed, and based on incorrect scientific conjectures. Iceland and Norway also ignored the whaling ban, and began killing whales some years later. Japan's approval of a scientific whaling permit was actually self-granted, without any other consideration or approval from the IWC. The "scientific permit" stated it requires the whale meat from the "scientific programme" to be sold or given away. It certainly doesn't take a genius to work out that this was a permit to sell whale meat, just like the good old days of Japan's commercial whaling operations. Giving the meat away for free helped marketing projects, thereby encouraging more consumption of whale meat. Norway honoured the IWC's whaling ban until 1993, when it found a loophole in the International Convention for the Regulation of Whaling. Like Japan, Norway set its own catch quotas, and set their target for more than 1000 minke whales a year. Iceland withdrew from the IWC, but rejoined in 2004. In 2006, Iceland resumed commercial whaling, killing fin whales – which are an endangered species, and minke whales too. What is the purpose of having the IWC, when the three whaling countries set their own catch quotas in the name of "scientific research", or for their own whaling industry, and decide when and where to carry their intentions out? Why would a "scientific whaling programme" base its studies on the mass killing of different species of whales? Scientists do not need to kill whales to carry out their research. Samples can be collected from the skin of whales and whale faeces. Population estimates and trends can be gained from sighting surveys and photo-identification of individual whales and acoustic surveys. Why couldn't a majority of member countries of the IWC object to this wanton killing of whales by Japan, Norway, and Iceland, when a ban had been put in place to protect the whales? There was a very simple reason – Japan bought votes.

Australia instituted proceedings against Japan in May 2010 at the International Court of Justice (ICJ), accusing Japan of being "in breach of obligations assumed by Japan under the 1946 International Convention for the Regulation of Whaling and of other international obligations for the preservation of marine mammals and the marine environment." The ICJ is the principal judicial division of the United Nations based in The Hague, Netherlands, and settles legal disputes between countries. Basically, Australia accused Japan of pursuing "a large-scale program of whaling under the Second Phase of its Japanese Whale Research Programme, under Special Permit in the Antarctic (JARPA II)." The United Nations court suggested that JARPA II could broadly be described as a "scientific research" programme. But was it for purposes of scientific research, when lethal methods were used? The court decided that the programme and implementation were not reasonable in establishing its stated "research objectives". Therefore, the special permits issued by Japan for the killing, taking, and treating of whales associated with JARPA II were not granted "for purposes of scientific research pursuant to Article VIII, paragraph 1, of the 1946 Convention". Since JARPA II was an ongoing programme, the ICJ ordered Japan to revoke any existing authorisation, permit, or licence to kill, take, or treat whales in relation to JARPA and to "refrain from granting any further permits under Article VIII of the Convention, in pursuance of that programme". Basically, the ICJ found a lack of scientific merit in Japan's whaling programme – something which the IWC anti-whaling members had been pointing out since 1986.

Japan's whaling ships returned to Japan with no catch after the United Nations court's decision. It was the first return without a catch since 1987. The IWC, at its 65th meeting, voted by 35 votes to 20 votes to put any future "scientific whaling" programmes to the IWC's scientific committee and the biennial commission itself for guidance. But Japanese diplomats said they would not be bound by the ICJ's resolution. Japan had taken a different interpretation of the ICJ ruling, and proceeded with a new round of "research whaling" in the Southern Ocean, as they had already declared. It is quite astounding that Japan was arrogant enough to ignore the rulings of an international organisation that they have controlled and corrupted for decades, not to mention the United Nations court.

In 2018, Japan declared that they thought the IWC should revise its zero-catch quota on whales. In other words, they thought the IWC should lift the ban on killing whales. Basically, the Japanese were saying, 'If we cannot dress up commercial whaling as "scientific research" let's go back to putting quotas in place for killing whales.' The 67th meeting of the IWC was held at Florianopolis, Brazil in September 2018. Japan and its pro-whaling allies tried to establish a working group to look at re-starting commercial hunts. Their attempts to sabotage the ban on commercial whaling backfired on them. There was heated debate, and afterwards Japan's idea was rejected by a clear majority of countries. This was finally confirmation that the role of the IWC was to serve as a conservation-focused organisation. Japan officially informed the IWC at the end of 2018 that it would be resuming commercial whaling from July 2019, and withdrawing from the IWC in effect on 30th June 2019. It was a political move, sending the message that Japan could do what it wanted across the world's oceans. For years, Japan has threatened to leave the IWC when it didn't get its own way. This time they were going ahead. Their decision brought international condemnation from conservationists from around the world, and from many other countries, including the UK and Australia. It was seen by many that Japan was "throwing its toys out of the pram" in response to not getting its own way, after dominating the IWC to its own ends for decades.

Ritual slaughter of pilot whales in the Faroe Islands

The population of the Faroe Islands numbers about 50,000 people, spread across 18 rocky volcanic islands between Iceland and Norway. It's been a self-governed nation since 1948, under the sovereignty of the King of Denmark. The Faroe Islands has a good standard of living, and is ranked among the highest in the world based on GDP per capita. The majority of Faroese have Danish passports. They are under Danish control, yet they don't see themselves as members of the EU, even though Denmark is an EU country. Therefore, they don't feel obliged to uphold EU law relating to the Convention on the Conservation of European Wildlife and Natural Habitats, where the killing of cetaceans is prohibited. The Faroese have been historically dependent on fishing and whale hunting, and even on hunting seabirds. Even today, their traditional methods of hunting whales, which go back centuries, are still fiercely defended – despite outrage from the rest of the world.

If you read the tourist websites, they are keen to play down the brutal and barbaric slaughter of the pilot whale population in the Faroe Islands during the summer months each year. They claim there are approximately 778,000 pilot whales in the North Atlantic, of which 100,000 can be found around the waters of the Faroe Islands. As the Faroese only catch 800 pilot whales a year on average, they maintain the tradition is sustainable. The problem is that the whale hunts take out entire family groups and populations of migratory marine species, which are difficult to count. The claim of 778,000 pilot whales was a population estimate that goes back to 1997. Apparently whaling has been regulated for centuries in the Faroe Islands, and "the law explicitly states that the hunt is to be conducted in such a way as to cause as little suffering to the whales as possible." As a "community based activity" the meat and blubber from the killing of the whales is shared amongst those that have helped to kill them. Again, this is something the Faroese have been doing for about a thousand years.

During their migration, pilot whales swim close to the shores of the Faroe Islands. The islanders are always on the lookout for pods of whales. When they see the whales, they will alert other islanders, who will rush out to surround the whales in a fleet of motorboats and dinghies. They then herd the whales towards one of 17 designated bays. As the sea becomes shallower near the shore, the pods of whales are stranded. The islanders stride into the water with ropes and hooks to help drag the whales onto the shore. The attackers systematically stab the whales with knives. Once they are dying, metal hooks are driven into the blowholes of the stranded whales. They are then dragged onto the beach and slaughtered by cutting their spines with long knives. Whole families of whales are slaughtered, and some younger whales swim around in their family members' blood for hours. There is an innate sense of loyalty amongst the pilot whales, and if one whale is stranded having been dragged onto the shore, the other whales will remain with the stricken mammal even if they endanger themselves. Tragically, by sticking together, the outcome is that they die together. We know that whales and dolphins are sentient beings, and that they can feel pain, fear, and loss – just the same as humans can. The hunt or the "Grind" draws crowds, including very young children, who help or watch the slaughter of the whales.

While the world largely sees the Faroese as acting in a primitive and sadistic fashion, this does not seem to bother the islanders. Protesters from outside the Faroe Islands are not welcome. Their cameras are usually grabbed from them and smashed at the whale hunts. Sea Shepherd Conservation Society campaigned a few years ago to stop the practice, by keeping watch and finding pods of whales before the islanders – chasing them further out to sea so as to scare them away from the armed islanders. The Faroese were furious, and called in the help of the Danish navy. The navy helped to arrest the members of Sea Shepherd, and held them overnight in jail. Their boats and high tech equipment were also confiscated. Sea Shepherd have vowed to continue their protests and opposition to the Grind and the barbarity of the pilot whale hunts, until they are stopped for good. Luckily, Sea Shepherd has refused to give up on the pilot whale hunts, and in 2017 they filed an infringement proceeding against Demark with the European Commission. They rightly claim that, as the killing, harming or harassment of cetaceans is prohibited across Europe under the Habitats Directive, Denmark is breaking the law. The same pilot whales that swim in the waters of the Faroe Islands also swim in EU waters. If a Danish person killed that whale, and the Danish government upheld that killing, then Denmark should be found guilty under the Habitats Directive. If Sea Shepherd are successful with their infringement proceedings, then Denmark will no longer be able to provide naval support and protection for the Grind. Hence, conservation groups will then be able to go back to the Faroe Islands and continue with their actions to stop the slaughter of the pilot whales.

As it happens, the Faroese may in fact stop hunting the whales by themselves. Research over the last 30 years on the Faroe Islands has proved unconditionally that eating whale meat and blubber can actually make the islanders seriously ill. In some cases, eating whale meat is fatal for humans. Pollution in the sea is so high that for every gram of whale meat, you can find 2 micrograms of methylmercury. A doctor has been examining islanders from birth, with regular checks throughout their lives for this period, and has discovered that the mercury has a negative impact on their cognitive functions, their reaction time, language, and their IQ. It also increases the risk of Parkinson's disease. The whales that are being eaten are so polluted by global activity, that it is endangering Faroese lives. His recommendation, in 2012, was for the Faroese to stop eating pilot whale meat and blubber. But still, the slaughter still goes on.

Inhumane slaughter of dolphins in Taiji, Japan

The Japanese have hunted cetaceans for hundreds of years, going all the way back to the fourteenth century, using basic equipment like simple nets and handheld harpoons. In the small town of Taiji, coastal whale hunts can be traced back to the early 1600s. Scrolls in the Taiji museum depict dozens of decorated boats in pursuit of a whale big enough to feed the community for months. Yet it has only been in the last hundred years that Japan has carried out the practice of commercial whaling. The shameful dolphin hunt of Taiji has only been established since 1969, though the Japanese government tells the world its Taiji tradition goes back centuries. The locals in Taiji, of which there were 3,428 at the last count in 2011, will tell you it's an all-important part of their economy and a "sacred cultural tradition".

The Japanese government have also told local fishermen in Taiji that the dolphins are responsible for the depletion of the fishing stocks. Hence, the slaughter of the dolphins for six months of the year – the fishermen think the dolphins are a pest and that the numbers need controlling. But the truth is that the fishermen have overfished their waters for years. Combined with sea pollution, this has led to there being less fish in coastal seas close to the shores. The Taiji hunters hijack the dolphins along their migratory route, using a flotilla of boats and banging poles to lead the dolphins astray and towards their cove – where the dolphins are slaughtered. Up until recently, the population of Taiji was unaware of what really went on with the dolphin slaughter. But over the years, with more and more animal activists around the world spreading the information through film and social media, this holocaust for dolphins is now out in the open. This has resulted in some Japanese activists now protesting about this ugly secret. It's ironic, because Taiji has dolphin symbols, images, and statues everywhere – including a whale museum depicting a town that appears to be very fond of dolphins and whales. But the sad reality is that the dolphins are being savagely killed, with only a handful from each hunt surviving. These survivors are exploited and abused, before being taken into captivity and sent to dolphinariums and tourist resorts all over the world. A dolphin slaughtered for meat may be worth $800, but a dolphin with unblemished skin, trained in the basics of eating dead fish from the hand of a trainer, can be worth $150,000. Taiji now relies on the income it makes from selling dolphins into captivity to fund their schools, services for the elderly, and so on. Only a modest income is made from the sale of dolphin meat, as it has become less popular with the younger generations of Japan, especially since people are discovering how contaminated dolphin meat is from the high mercury/pollution levels in the sea. But still, the dolphin hunts continue, turning the waters of Taiji red.

Anybody who has an ounce of compassion for dolphins should watch the award winning film "The Cove". This was awarded "Best Documentary Feature" in 2010, and shows the outrageous capture and slaughter of dolphins in all its evil. The film follows Ric O'Barry's quest to document the dolphin hunting in Taiji, and bring it to the attention of the world. The release of the film caused an international outcry, with the documentary winning an Oscar. It can be watched for free on YouTube. Ric O Barry, founder of the "Dolphin Project", spent ten years training and looking after dolphins for the television series "Flipper" from the 1960s and other projects with dolphins. After his favourite dolphin Kathy died in his arms, he realised that capturing dolphins and training them to perform silly tricks was intrinsically wrong. From that time onwards, he has spent nearly 50 years trying to rescue and rehabilitate dolphins across the world to be released back into the wild. He has also vigorously campaigned to stop the Taiji dolphin hunts for good.

Before we get into what happens on the dolphin hunts, we should be aware of a more recent documentary. "A Whale of a Tale" is a documentary looking at the dolphin hunts from a Japanese perspective. Megumi Sasaki, a New York-based documentary film maker from Japan was shocked to see "The Cove" in 2009. Her stance was that this little town had been hard done by, thanks to the Hollywood film crew with a multimillion-dollar budget. For her, it wasn't quite right to try to force the cessation of Taiji's long-standing customs, that would mean the town losing their jobs, food culture, and an identity and pride they had inherited over centuries. She was further disturbed about how almost overnight Taiji became the most-go-to destination and battlefield for activists, who were flocking there from all over the world.

As you've probably gathered, it's a complex situation, with divisions between the east and the west, international activists, and journalists, on issues about nature and wildlife. Megumi Sasaki points out that whaling was the first major global business, where many countries across the globe hunted nearly all the large whales to extinction by the 1930s. Back then, the whales were hunted for their oil. Then, in the 1970s, "save the whale" slogans and other representations made whales the great symbol of environmental campaigns. Sasaki claims it took her 'six years of meticulous research and hundreds of interviews' to get the information for her documentary. "A Whale of a Tale" focuses largely on points of contact and communication between the two sides around the issue of dolphin hunting in Taiji. The documentary is not just about the blood and gore of the dolphin slaughter, but shows the fishermen and people of Taiji as human beings in their homes with their families. The locals have concerns about how much mercury is in the dolphin meat, and even ask if the dolphins are endangered. Sasaki's documentary presents the subject really well, with less emotion and subjectivity, and gives both sides equal chance to express their views.

So, onto the hunt itself. The dolphin hunting season for Taiji takes place every year, from 1st September to the end of March. During that time, about 2,000 dolphins are hunted and brutally killed. The Japanese Fisheries Agency issues permits to fishermen to hunt more than 20,000 small whales, dolphins, and porpoises each year around the coasts in Japan. In Taiji, about 30 fishermen or dolphin hunters take part in the hunt, and they go out in motorised boats at the crack of dawn to search for dolphins. They head out to deeper water, where the dolphins can be found on the migratory paths that they have used for thousands and thousands of years. The boats are spread out, but evenly spaced. When a pod of dolphins swim by, the hunters lower their stainless steel poles into the water on either side of each boat. Then the hunters repeatedly hit the poles with hammers, which makes a wall of sound between the boats and the shoreline. The dolphins are desperate to get away from the sounds, and so they swim towards the shore. Dolphin hunters then drive them into the small hidden cove near Taiji harbour, and the huntsmen trap the dolphins by securing nets across the cove so the dolphins cannot leave.

The dolphins are frantic, and activist monitors have recorded the heavy flapping of their tails on the water and their cries for help as they become frantic with fear. The dolphins are usually left overnight whilst the dolphin hunters go home, get their rest and sleep. The next day, the hunters return to kill and butcher the dolphins. This is usually done away from prying eyes, because the cove is out of bounds to the public. They also use a range of tarpaulins to cover the dolphins, to hide what goes on, and to prevent cove monitors filming whilst they kill them. Once the killing starts, the dolphins thrash about in their blood and they scream out in fear and pain. The dolphin hunters used to kill them with long sharp spears, but they changed their methods after "The Cove" was released to the world. These days they use sharp metal spikes, which they thrust into the dolphins behind the blowholes. Then they push wooden corks into the wounds, to avoid the blood spurting out into the waters of the cove. How anyone can believe that this is a humane way of killing the dolphins is beyond all reason. Film footage from hidden cameras has shown the dolphins thrashing around in agony for several minutes. Cove monitors have witnessed dolphins still alive, even when they have been dragged to the slaughterhouse.

Sometimes, the dolphins can be left in limbo for days with no food. This happens if dolphin trainers and members of the captivity industry want to view them and select certain dolphins. There is a wealth of video footage showing the hunters and the dolphin trainers having a joke and a laugh as they tie ropes around the flukes of dolphins, which they tie to their boats. They often drag them along with the boats, with their blowholes submerged under water. Often these injured dolphins cannot breathe. Pregnant dolphins and young calves are not spared. The dolphin trainers have been witnessed helping to slaughter the dolphins. One particular video showed graphic cruelty, with dolphin hunters and trainers running their small boats with outboard motors over the top of the dolphins, resulting in painful deep cuts and other injuries. The dolphins screamed and cried, whilst the dolphin hunters shrieked with laughter. Tormenting and causing pain appears to be normal for dolphin hunters. Unfortunately, it also seems to be acceptable behaviour for the dolphin trainers, who claim to "love dolphins".

Taiji dolphins are sold to aquariums, dolphinariums, hotels, and tourist venues around the world. Swim-with-dolphin programmes appear to be popular. Countries in which this can be done include Russia, Georgia, Ukraine, China, Korea, Vietnam, Turkey, United Arab Emirates, Qatar, Tunisia, Egypt, Iran, Saudi Arabia, Taiwan, and the Philippines. There is now a US law that outlaws importing dolphins from Taiji, because the capture of marine mammals should be humane. But there are suspicions that some of the imported marine mammals were originally from the Taiji dolphin hunts, even though they were bought from other aquariums and dolphinariums. Ultimately, the only way to stop the Taiji driven dolphin hunts is for tourists and members of the public to stop buying tickets to dolphin shows and to turn their backs on this insidious industry. All whales and dolphins belong in the wild. Don't continue their early deaths and wrongful captures by buying tickets to see dolphins performing.

The southern resident killer whales

The inland waterways of the Salish Sea in the Pacific Northwest, western North America, are home to a community of southern resident killer whales. They live in these waters from spring to autumn. There is a 45 member human taskforce, the "Southern Resident Killer Whale Task Force" which represents various organisations in the area. Recently, it has come together to help prevent these orcas becoming extinct. The latest figures show there are 75 orcas, making up three pods named J, K, and L. The group's numbers are at a 30-year low, with old members dying faster than new ones being born. No new babies have been born and survived since 2015. In 2005, the southern residents were listed as endangered under the *Endangered Species Act*. Many of the reproductive females have been dying off, leaving the group to decline further until it reaches a stage of "quasi-extinction" – meaning there are not enough animals left to sustain the population.

The southern residents are thought to be the most studied group of mammals in the world. They have had attention from scientists, naturalists, politicians, and whale-watchers for many years. They are also one of the most contaminated marine mammals in the world. Salmon accounts for 96% of their diet. The southern residents are contaminated by the pollutants in the fish they eat, which accumulate in their blubber. These pollutants include motor oil, chemicals from household products, pesticides, oil spills, and other toxic substances. They are also affected by noise pollution from ships, boats, and motor-power boats. This impacts their echolocation abilities, and due to the noise the whales feed less. There have been regulations requiring boats to stay more than 200 yards away from whales, but more could certainly be done to benefit them. Fat-rich Chinook salmon is the southern residents' preferred food. The scarcity and in some populations extinction of this salmon has posed serious threats to an already endangered species. The fish have a large range, from far inland streams to the expansive Pacific Ocean. Yet the Chinook have to cope with man-made dams, commercial fishing nets, toxic pollutants, and a rapid increase in the population of algae – causing algal blooms. If the killer whales cannot find enough Chinook to eat, they have to survive on blubber reserves in order to maintain their energy levels. State and federal agencies have been tasked with protecting these killer whales and their habitats; some whales been starving to death due to the perilous depletion of Chinook populations. Finding more Chinook and getting it to the killer whales has to be top priority. As the whales are burning up their blubber reserves, they are releasing toxic chemicals into their bloodstream. This in turn causes disarray to their immune, reproductive, and neurological systems, which is probably the underlying problem regarding lack of births in the last few years. The killer whales are starving, and they are showing all the signs of this, by looking emaciated and weak. Drastic situations call for drastic solutions, but there doesn't appear to be much headway in helping the killer whales at the moment. There are plenty of ideas floating around, but the solutions – from breeding more Chinook fish in hatcheries, to removing four dams on the lower Snake River in southeast Washington – are not going to be implemented or even agreed upon any time soon.

During July 2018, a 20-year-old female orca named Tahlequah (J35) gave birth to a female calf. It died with 30 minutes of being born. Tahlequah's grief for her baby calf was so great that it drew the attention of people from all over the world. It was heart breaking to see this grieving whale carrying the dead body of her calf for 17 days. 'I have never seen that kind of grief,' said Ken Balcomb from the Center of Whale Research. Killer whales are intelligent and complex social creatures. Members of Tahlequah's family helped her carry her dead calf, as they felt the same sense of grief as she did. At that point, there had been no babies born and surviving in the previous two years. Tahlequah's loss was her family's loss too. Back in 2010, Tahlequah had her first calf, and it was noted that she played with her more than most orca mothers would have played with their calves. Was Tahlequah sending a message to the world whilst carrying her dead calf for 17 days? Was she saying, 'Look how you are killing us'?

It's obvious to everyone that humans are killing the southern resident killer whales, and no one is doing anything constructive to defend and protect them. For decades, those tasked with protecting these whales knew the whales were starving. Whilst Tahlequah was parading her dead calf and showing her grief to the world, attention was being given to Scarlet (J50) a 4-year-old calf. She was emaciated, with her ribs showing, and on the edge of survival. She has been given shots of antibiotics, and scientists are hoping she will eat some Chinook salmon directly put in front of her. With the eyes of the world on these killer whale families, who are on the brink of extinction, can there really be a glimmer of hope for them? Perhaps, but only if we act.

The brutality of the whaling industry

In the last century, whales were brutally pushed to extinction by commercial whaling practises. The international moratorium on commercial whaling has been in force since 1986, but Japan, Norway and Iceland continue to ignore this. In the whaling industry of today, whales are chased to the point of exhaustion, and then hit by exploding harpoons to catch and haul them in. The technology for killing whales has barely changed since the nineteenth century. Back then, they used a grenade-tipped harpoon. In more modern times, the main killing weapon – the penthrite grenade harpoon – is fired from a cannon on the bow of a ship. The intention is for the harpoon to penetrate a foot into the whale before the explosion. This is unacceptably cruel, because the first hit is normally not fatal. So, the whales are hit by more exploding harpoons before they die. They are dragged to whaling vessels and then more harpoons and high-powered rifles are used to finish them off. They may appear to be unconscious, but they will be feeling unimaginable pain.

Whales are so large and powerful that the amount of force required to kill one is totally inhumane. Dr Lillie, who was a ship's physician on an Antarctic whaling expedition in 1946, wrote:

"If we can imagine a horse having two or three explosive spears stuck in its stomach and being made to pull a butcher's truck through the streets of London while it pours blood into the gutter, we shall have an idea of the method of killing. The gunners themselves admit that if whales could scream, the industry would stop, for nobody would be able to stand it."

The IWC defines "humane killing" as a process where death is brought about "without pain, stress or distress perceptible to the animal. That is the ideal. Any humane killing technique aims first to render an animal insensitive to pain as swiftly as is technically possible, which in practice cannot be instantaneous in the scientific sense."

The three countries continuing to catch whales say their methods are not cruel, and reject calls to end whaling. All three whaling countries are unlikely to share their hunting data with the IWC, since they are no longer members. That is also the case for the Aboriginal Subsistance Whaling (ASW), who are outside the IWC 1986 moratorium. This group is recognised as those native peoples who need to hunt whales at appropriate levels to their cultural and nutritional requirements around the world. But even these groups appear to be killing whales beyond the appropriate levels for their needs.

The report, *Troubled Waters*, clearly examines the animal welfare implications involved in modern whaling activities. A coalition of 142 animal welfare organisations from 57 countries, including Britain, came together in a coalition called "Whalewatch". The purpose was to bring the concerns to the IWC meeting in Italy in 2004, and maintain the moratorium on commercial whaling. Sir David Attenborough, in the foreword to the report, stated, "The following pages contain hard scientific dispassionate evidence that there is no humane way to kill a whale at sea." He also suggested that the reader should "decide for yourself whether the hunting of whales in this way should still be tolerated by a civilised society." There is no getting away from the facts. Whaling is a bloody and brutal occupation. There has been strong opposition to whaling from all over the world, but still Japan, Norway and Iceland continue to do it.

One of the most shameful whaling activities has been the killing of blue whales – almost to extinction – by commercial whaling. These whales can still be found in every ocean, but three specific populations are more numerous – those found in the North Atlantic, the North Pacific, and the Southern Hemisphere. It's been 50 years since hunting blue whales was finally banned (in 1966), but the blue whale has struggled to repopulate. The numbers of blue whales remain critical and they are now an endangered species. A report in 2002 suggested there were 5,000-12,000 blue whales left on our planet. The International Union for Conservation of Nature (IUCN) estimates there is now a population of between 10,000 and 25,000 blue whales in our oceans across the world. Before commercial whaling there was a population of up to 300,000 in the Antarctic seas. Today, there is probably a population of about 2000 blue whales in the Antarctic area.

The country of Iceland is also guilty of reprehensible crimes against whales. Their slaughter of fin whales is in defiance of the international ban on commercial whaling and flies in the face of outrage from countries around the world. Iceland has set a self-allocated quota of up to 161 fin whales. Whale meat is not in demand by Icelanders, but they are taking about 20% of the catch to feed tourists, with the remaining 80% being shipped to Japan. This is despite the ban on international trade in whale meat, under the Convention on International Trade in Endangered Species of Wild Fauna and Flora (CITES). It's quite unbelievable, especially when you consider that Iceland is proud of its nature tourism, yet their restaurants are serving up dishes of whale meat to tourists. UK visitors make up the biggest sector of the tourism market in Iceland. Whale watching is a booming industry in Iceland, and it's certainly fair to say that tourists would prefer to see whales in the wild than on the menu in restaurants. Taking into account that the latest polls show 34% of Icelanders are opposed to hunting whales, and the fact that prominent whaling companies have been making losses for some time, the future looks bleak for commercial whaling in Iceland. Yet, is it really so bleak? Iceland set new quotas at the beginning of 2019 for hunting minke and fin whales. The government is allowing 217 minke whales and 209 fin whales to be harpooned every year, until 2023. According to Iceland's Marine Research Institute, the quotas are based on scientific research. Furthermore, they claim these quotas are sustainable, monitored, and in line with international law. These claims don't really add up, however, when you consider that the demand for whale meat is so low. In the short term, Icelandic whaling may be propped up by various companies and shareholders, but everyone knows that companies cannot survive losing money year after year.

According to Norway, there are more than 100,000 minke whales in Norwegian waters. However, Norway's commercial whaling has failed to meet its quotas for hunting minke whales in recent years. Is this a sign of less minke whales in Norwegian waters? Or could it be because there is a falling demand for whale meat in Norway? There is a theory that minke whales are swimming to colder waters because of climate change, but whaling experts say that Norway is failing to meet its annual quotas because there is insufficient capacity of whale meat processing plants. Still, that doesn't stop the Norwegian government setting high targets for quotas. A quota of 1,278 whales has been set for 2019. Whatever the reason for setting high quotas, the industry is in decline, and perhaps Norway should consider whaling a thing of the past. The whalers rely on government subsidies, and have been targeting young people and tourists to keep their ailing industry alive. One of the efforts was to introduce products like whale sushi and whale burgers at international music festivals, but efforts have flopped. Interestingly, before the ban on commercial whaling in 1986, Norway exported over

50% of its whale products to Japan, and some of its whale meat went to the Faroe Islands. But in more recent years there has been research into the contamination by sea pollutants in minke whale meat. With no demand for whale meat by Norwegians, why is the Norwegian government determined to keep their whaling industry active? It appears that Norway is feeding whale meat to foxes and mink (who are reared for their fur on farms). They are also feeding said meat to sled dogs, and using it as pet food. They are still exporting some whale meat to Japan, though there has been some concern regarding contaminated meat due to pollution in the seas. Perhaps the whaling industry is relying on government subsidies to keep people in jobs, but that is not helping conservation efforts on the planet. Nor will it help Norway get back on track with commercial whaling in the foreseeable future. Let's hope the end of cruel and barbaric whale hunting in Norway is in sight.

Likewise, Japan carries out "scientific research" in place of commercial whaling, but there doesn't seem to be any difference between the two. Whales are captured and killed, whatever Japan wants to name the practice. Demand for whale meat is decreasing as the population gets older, and there is the same problem with contamination of whale meat. It's all very similar to the future of whaling in Iceland and Norway. Interviews on the streets in Japanese towns have revealed there is a divide between the younger and older generations. In the past, the older generation ate whale meat because it was cheap and a good source of protein after World War II. Japan had very little resources, and food was scarce. Whale meat was even used for school dinners and sold at the markets. Younger generations are rather equivocal. Some have eaten a small amount of whale meat for school dinners, and some have never tried it. The general opinion is that every Japanese person has probably eaten whale meat at least once in their lifetime. On the whole, about 10% of Japanese people still eat whale meat, and that includes those who eat it once every six months.

Nowadays, whale meat is an expensive dish in restaurants and bistro-pubs. If it was put on a plate in front of them, most of the younger Japanese say they would try it and some would eat the whole meal. But with the choice of other popular meats like pork and chicken, there isn't any necessity to eat whale. In a survey, a large group of Japanese people were quizzed about the world's opposition to whaling. Many of them were surprised, and nearly all of them had no idea there had been a global ban on catching whales since 1986. Most didn't know about the ruling against Japan's scientific whaling from the International Court of Justice. Some Japanese had a vague idea about the opposition to their country's whaling activity, but the majority were unaware. They certainly didn't think whales would become extinct, and said their country was probably keeping an eye on the situation. What was refreshing to hear them say, was that they didn't think Japanese companies should profit from illegal whaling. The majority of the younger Japanese surveyed did know about some activists campaigning, and were angry about Japan's whaling and dolphin hunting. But the older Japanese said that each country is different, and that we have no right to judge Japan. They claimed that other countries should just accept it as part of the Japanese culture. But they did think whaling will ultimately decline, because people would eventually stop eating whale meat. There was no mention from any participants in any of the age groups about contamination of whale and dolphin meat. There appears to be a lot of things the government prefers to keep under wraps, and it is quite deplorable that the Japanese don't get the opportunity to know that by eating whale meat they could be putting their health at risk.

The vaquita, the most endangered marine mammal in the world

This little delicate porpoise is on the edge of extinction. It was officially discovered in 1958, and 60 years later we are on the brink of losing them forever. More than half the population has been lost in the last three years. How crazy is that? Sadly, they are being caught and drowned in gillnets used by illegal fishing operations within Mexico's Gulf of California, ironically in areas which are marine protected. The vaquita has a large dark ring around each of its eyes, and is known as the "senorita of the sea" or the "panda of the ocean". The word vaquita means "little cow" in Spanish. It's about 4 feet long, and weighs less than 100 lbs. It can be found off the coast of Baja, Mexico. They like the shallow waters close to the shore, but they are quick to swim away if a boat approaches.

Sea Shepherd wanted tourists to visit the town of San Felipe in Baja, because it was thought the tourist dollars could help save the vaquita. Tourism could provide jobs for the residents, which would take the pressure off those who were illegally setting nets and fishing. But local fishermen were angry, and they thought Sea Shepherd was going to force them out of the Gulf of California. The Mexican navy and police smoothed things over and provided security to Sea Shepherd ships and crew. As Sea Shepherd were the only group with a presence in the area, they were the object of the fishermen's anger. There had been fishing restrictions imposed to help save the vaquita, but the compensation was not seen as adequate for the fishermen. The ban continued, and it was the federal government's intention to put in force a permanent ban on gillnets in that part of the gulf. The navy, the environmental protection agency Profepa, and the Environmental Police, stepped up their surveillance to prevent illegal fishing. It is this illegal fishing that has been the reason for the sharp decline in the vaquita numbers in the last few years. Sea Shepherd have continued to pull up the illegal gillnets under an agreement with the Mexican government. Unfortunately, these intensive efforts may be too late to save the vaquita.

It is now acknowledged that the vaquita has become the victim of the illegal wildlife trade, because it is so lucrative, along with the totoaba, a marine fish endemic to the Gulf of California. The totoaba is a similar size to the vaquita, and its bladder can fetch up to 10,000 dollars. Why? Well, there are claims that fish bladders have amazing properties. You won't be surprised to learn that these claims are completely unsubstantiated, but due to marketing, elite and wealthy Chinese people are falling for the lies. There are no proven benefits, but it is illegal and expensive, so they think it must be good for your health. With such a lucrative pay-out, local fishermen are using gillnets to catch as many as possible.

In 2011, there were 600 vaquita. By 2015, the population was down to 60. In 2017, there were only 30. In 2018, there were only 12 left in the world, and in 2019 the number could be down to single figures. A team of marine mammal scientists had an idea to capture a couple of vaquita and put them into sea pens, hoping they would multiply. They captured their first vaquita aged about 6 months, and put it in the pen. Unfortunately she was so agitated that they had to release her. A second captured vaquita stopped breathing, such was the stress of being caught. They tried for 3 hours to resuscitate her, but she died. The project was then stopped, because they couldn't afford to lose another one.

If the vaquita cannot be protected by bringing them into a safe and secure environment monitored by experts, then unfortunately marine scientists think it's really too late to save the species. They hope to have learnt lessons for the future of other species. They acted too late in establishing collaboration and cooperation between agencies, to ensure the safeguarding of a credible population. The reality is, we will lose this beautiful and exquisite porpoise forever – and all thanks to illegal activities and human greed. Just another terrible tragedy for our precious planet.

A few last words ...

There is a campaign for intelligent marine mammals to have a right to life. A number of scientists and academics believe that whales and dolphins should be protected under international law as "non-humans", with a legally enforceable right to life and liberty, based on their high intelligence and emotional empathy. Like humans, cetaceans have an individual sense of self. Therefore, they should not be held in captivity or servitude, and should not be hunted down and killed. They should not be subjected to cruelty, and they should have the right to stay in their natural environment. Furthermore, they cannot be the property of any state, corporation, human group, or individual.

If other endangered mammals, whether on land or sea, are to avoid the fate of the vaquita, we must act quickly. We need a blueprint in place, to save the co-habitants of our planet.

SEA SHEPHERD   Website: www.seashepherd.org

Email: info@seashepherd.org   **Registered Charity: Non-profit organisation**

"Established in 1977, Sea Shepherd Conservation Society (SSCS) is an international non-profit, marine wildlife conservation organisation. Our mission is to end the destruction of habitat and slaughter of wildlife in the world's oceans in order to conserve and protect ecosystems and species.

Sea Shepherd uses innovative direct-action tactics to investigate, document, and take action when necessary to expose and confront illegal activities on the high seas. By safeguarding the biodiversity of our delicately balanced ocean ecosystems, Sea Shepherd works to ensure their survival for future generations."

RIC O'BARRY'S DOLPHIN PROJECT   Website: www.dolphinproject.com

Email: contact@dolphinproject.com   **Registered Charity: Non-profit organisation**

"The mission of Dolphin Project is to end dolphin exploitation and slaughter, as dolphins are routinely captured, harassed, slaughtered and sold into captivity around the world – all in the name of profit. Dolphin Project works not only to halt these slaughters, but also to rehabilitate captive dolphins for retirement and/or release, investigate and advocate for economic alternatives to dolphin slaughter, and to put a permanent end to dolphin captivity."

WHALE AND DOLPHIN CONSERVATION   Website: www.whales.org

Email: info@whales.org   Registered Charity No: 1014705

"WDC's work combines concern for the welfare of individual whales, dolphins and porpoises with efforts to ensure the protection of the species, populations and their habitats. We conduct research, provide advice to decision makers about how to protect the animals and fund conservation and education projects around the world, working for solutions which benefit people and animals."

INTERNATIONAL FUND FOR ANIMAL WELFARE (IFAW)   Website: www.ifaw.org

Email: info-uk@ifaw.org   Registered Charity No: 1024806

"Our vision is a world where animals are respected and protected. With offices in 15 countries and projects in more than 40 countries, we rescue individual animals, safeguard populations, preserve habitat and advocate for a better future."

CHAPTER SIX
Captive Animals

"The only good cage is an empty cage."

Laurence Anthony

What is wrong with keeping wild animals in captivity?

Keeping animals in captivity is an abhorrent practice. Why should animals spend their entire lives in confinement, just for our amusement or our desire to see them close up? Is it really necessary to keep animals in captivity in this day and age, when we have excellent quality wildlife documentaries on film, TV, and the internet, and we can go on eco-safaris and see wild animals in their natural habitat? In the wild, it can be harsh and cruel, but wild animals have evolved to live in their indigenous environments. At the other end of the spectrum, we have wild animals in zoos and safari parks, where they are kept in basic enclosures for the ticket-paying public. Some are trained to perform tricks similar to those animals in a circus, because the public expect to be amused and it helps to boost ticket sales. There is a lot of talk about zoos and safari parks being important for education, research, and conservation. But the general consensus is that many of the establishments pay lip service to these ideals. They talk a good game (through their websites, adverts, and promotions) about securing the welfare of species, and are overwhelmingly perceived by the public as "entertaining". But the reality, as ever, is different.

Providing wild animals in captivity with what they need is no easy task, and in some cases impossible. Take circuses for example. How can a circus keep wild animals such as lions and tigers, as well as camels and zebras, in the best environment? They are expected to perform tricks for the paying public night after night, and spend time training day after day when on the road. Lions and tigers are kept in small cages, and are transported on "beast wagons" covering hundreds of miles a week. None of this mimics any features or aspect of their natural environment in the wild. Placing animals in situations that are unsuitable for their welfare only causes them to suffer stress and behavioural problems. Being fed an inadequate diet, whilst travelling, will make the animals ill. When combined with the stress and fear that these animals experience, this can result in death.

The World Association of Zoos and Aquariums (WAZA) states on its home web page, "The world zoo and aquarium community welcomes over 700 million visitors annually across the globe." This equates to about 11% of the global human population, with approximately one in ten of us visiting a zoo or aquarium every year. In the UK, our representation for WAZA is the British & Irish Association of Zoos & Aquariums (BIAZA): "The professional body representing the best zoos and aquariums in Britain and Ireland. We have over 100 zoo and aquarium members who pride themselves on their excellent animal welfare, education and conservation work." Consider then that this leaves a significant number of licensed "zoos and aquariums" which are not represented by BIAZA in the UK. The mind boggles at just how many captive animals there must be in the world. Unfortunately, a highly significant number of wild animals do not belong to zoos and aquariums which are members of professional organisations. In many countries "zoos" can be set up without government licences, and those countries that do insist on issuing licences don't necessarily follow up with routine inspections. Then there are some countries who have little or no welfare laws in place to protect animals from abuse and neglect. Their captive animals can be subject to a life of constant suffering and death.One of the more notorious zoos on the planet, Surabaya Zoo, is a 37-hectare zoo located in the city of Surabaya in East Java, Indonesia. There have been numerous newspaper articles, TV reports and social media responses across the world over the state of the zoo's emaciated and starving wild animals. Many are skeletal, but the zoo is still open to the paying public. It has been described as a 'virtual hell on earth for animals' and 'the zoo of death', with 50 animals at the zoo dying in just a three-month period. A giraffe died from eating 20 kilos of litter that had been thrown into his pen. A Sumatran tiger starved to death after his digestive tract rotted away from being fed meat laced with formaldehyde. A young lion hung himself in his cage, by getting his neck tangled in a cable that his keepers used to open and close the door. Despite the atrocities and pleas from countries and charities around the world, including WAZA, the zoo is still open for business. It seems the local government officials reject the notion that their zoo is a national shame. As far as they are concerned, they can only talk about its successes.

Tourism

When they see the sad plight of animals in wildlife attractions, tourists should walk away and complain to their travel companies. By doing so, they would actually be helping the animals. If there was no money to be made from exploiting animals, then there would be no tourist attractions involving animals. If tourists didn't buy tickets to marine parks, said parks would close down and marine life could stay in the oceans where it belongs. The same applies to zoos, riding elephants, taking selfies with tigers, petting lion cubs, and so on. The abuse and exploitation would no longer exist, because the people running these tourist-based enterprises wouldn't make any money from them. Their business would have to cease if there were few or no paying customers. But tourists are actually fuelling this cruel and desperate abuse of wildlife. The charity

World Animal Protection (WAP) commissioned research carried out by the University of Oxford's Wildlife Conservation Research Unit (WildCRU). They estimated there were about 550,000 wild animals across the world in irresponsible and cruel tourist attractions.

"They compared expert scientific reviews of wildlife tourism venues with more than 50,000 tourist reviews on TripAdvisor. This revealed that 80% of people left positive reviews for venues that are treating wild animals cruelly."

The research also stated that welfare or conservation abuses were happening in approximately three out of every four attractions included in the study. So, why do tourists not pick up on the suffering of wild animals at these venues? The problem is that many of the tourists supporting these wildlife attractions probably love animals, but they don't know the truth about what is going on. If they were aware of what goes on behind the scenes, there would probably be a significant number who would purposely avoid these tourist attractions, thus making it less viable for said attractions to exist.

Many of the animals at wildlife attractions are taken away from their mothers when they are babies. Some are taken from their mother at birth, like lion cubs used for petting. They are hand reared, so they are tame enough when small to be handled by tourists, including children. Baby elephants have to endure a ghastly training process called "the crush". They are subjected to severe pain, physical restraints, and left without food and water to break their spirit – and all this begins when they are a small baby. All of this, just for a life of carrying tourists up and down a track or road, and performing a few silly tricks. If they are not carrying tourists or performing, then they are chained up and unable to socially interact with other elephants. Is a few minutes sitting on the back of an elephant worth the years of pain and misery these creatures suffer?

In Thailand, there are nearly 1,000 tigers in seventeen venues, catering for people wanting a selfie with a tiger cub. These cubs are taken away from their mothers as small babies. They are then handled, hugged, and pulled around by tourists. There seems to be a fixation with tourists for taking selfies with a wild animal. The result is a photo that can be sent around the world to all their Facebook friends, showing off their face with a new little tiger buddy. When the tiger cubs are not being selfie props, they are chained in small bare cages. As they get older they are allegedly drugged, so people can sit next to them and have a photo taken to share on social media. Adult tigers are also trained to perform for tourists – but the training itself is done in unnatural and distressing ways. According to reports, this vile tourist industry is growing year on year in Thailand. If only tourists would turn their backs on this abuse and stop paying for photos and tiger performances, this could realistically stem the growing systematic abuse of these wild animals.

One of the worst examples of the abuse of tigers in Thailand was the notorious "Tiger Temple" which was closed down at the end of May 2016. Twenty years previously, the monks of the Buddhist temple started taking in tiger cubs because poachers had killed their mothers. Villagers continued to bring tigers to the temple, which grew and developed into a lucrative tourist attraction. It was fronted as an admission charging "zoo" where tourists paid to have their photos taken with the tigers. They could pet them, feed them, and walk them around on leads. The adult tigers were allegedly heavily sedated, and many were found almost lifeless around the temple. The monks claimed they were sleeping. Based on suspicion that the monks were trafficking tiger parts, the temple was raided. Officials found 40 frozen tiger cub carcasses in a freezer, a further 20 tiger cubs floating in jars of formaldehyde, plus numerous tiger body parts and carcasses of other animals. From the raid, they removed 147 tigers, and intercepted a monk trying to flee Thailand with a truckload of tiger fangs and skins. The temple may have been closed down, but within months plans were made to open a new tiger zoo next door to the temple. The new zoo is not legally connected to the old temple, (which was under the business name Tiger Temple Co. Ltd) because it changed the name to Golden Tiger (Thailand) Co. Ltd in February 2017. But it appears to be the same monks running the new venture. The only difference being that they are not keeping the tigers in the temple, and they have to adhere to stricter regulations. So, the misery for the tigers continues as before.

Walking with and handling lion cubs tends to be most prominent on ranches in South Africa, but there are also venues in other African states. Tourists are allowed to handle the cubs and pose for photos. If the cubs, obviously being playful at this age, get out of hand and become aggressive, trainers discipline them. The cubs are trained on leads. Some of the older lions are taken out on walks with tourists. There have been fatalities amongst tourists out on these lion walks, but still this industry goes on. These lions will never be released into the wild as adults, but the tourists are probably unaware of what happens to the adult lions when they are no longer safe for petting. The petting farms are the front end of canned lion ranches. What tourists and even young volunteers are unaware of, is that the adult lions are usually left in compounds on the ranches.

Some may not be fed properly or given any veterinary treatment. As babies, they are exploited, and good money is made from tourists who pay to spend time with them. As adults, they will be shot by visiting trophy hunters, for thousands and thousands of dollars. It seems there is always a dark side for wildlife at tourist attractions.

Marine parks

"Marine park" is a generic term for large aquariums or dolphinariums that house cetaceans like dolphins and whales. Like zoos, marine parks are open to the ticket-paying public, which accounts for the best part of all their revenue. So, obviously it is important for these venues to get as many people as possible through their gates, to see dolphins and whales kept in small and inadequate tanks. In their natural environment, dolphins and whales live in complex social groups, in the open oceans around the world. All captive dolphins and whales have been torn away from their families in the wild, to live a life in isolation at these tourist venues. In about 60 countries across the world, there are over 2000 dolphins kept in small tanks. Most of these dolphins will have been captured by dolphin hunters in Taiji. There are approximately 60 killer whales in captivity in marine parks across the world, in similarly deplorable small tanks.

Each day in the wild, dolphins can travel about 80-100 miles. Similarly, a killer whale can travel over 100-140 miles a day. Back at the marine parks, the dolphins and whales are kept in such small tanks that they can only swim in circles. In the USA, the law states that dolphins should have a tank with a dimension of 28 feet width and 7 feet depth. But because the tanks are so small, when the dolphins make a whistling noise the sound is echoed back to them, and it can make them go literally mad having to listen to the echo effect. There is a strong argument that killer whales are too big to be kept in captivity. In the USA, the law requires that tanks be at least 12 feet deep and 48 feet in diameter, which is woefully insufficient for any size killer whale.

Bottlenose dolphins make great animals for entertainment in marine parks, because they appear playful and social. But people need to understand that dolphins in captivity are living a very stressful life in these artificial surroundings. Seemingly healthy dolphins in captivity can die at an early age without warning. Very few captive dolphins live to an old age, and those that do are expected to continue performing until they die. Generally, dolphins are forced to work around 12 hours a day performing in the pool for audiences. Between performances they are used for sessions in the petting pools. These can be very noisy and chaotic, especially when you have excited children holding up small fish to feed the dolphins. By deliberately keeping the fish small, the dolphins will keep coming back for more. Dolphins will beg for the fish, because they are deliberately underfed to encourage them to perform, by way of giving them food rewards. Even sensible tourists can touch dolphins in rough or painful ways. Hence, tourists are bitten and injured by dolphins. On the other hand, dolphins can also be harmed by rubbish that is either deliberately thrown into the dolphin pool or accidentally dropped in the pool. Marine parks make a lot of money by charging extortionate fees for the petting programmes. Fortunately for some dolphins, many of the parks have shut down their petting pools because of the abusive behaviour by some tourists and the fact that it is inherently unsafe for both tourists and dolphins. But dolphin petting still goes on in marine parks across the world, because it is highly profitable.

Swimming with dolphins has been hailed as once in a lifetime experience that you will never forget. The marine parks offer swimming with a bottlenose dolphin as a 30 minute adventure, including an educational documentary and one-to-one with a professional trainer in the dolphin pool, or a shorter experience if required. Dolphins are expected to do 3 or more of these half-hour sessions a day, as well as the main performances for large audiences. These unnatural interactions for dolphins, who are already stressed and depressed with the tyranny of living in a marine park, are cruel and callous. Their dolphin pools are chlorinated so that tourists can swim with them and take home enchanting photos of their magical experiences. Chlorine is put in the water to keep the water sparkly clear and free of algae and bacteria. Slowly, the dolphins and killer whales are wasting away with eye problems and the effects on their internal organs. It also impacts sea lions and walruses, who don't have any effective eye protection, often suffering from cataracts and corneal diseases as a result – largely caused by chlorine and other water treatments. Unsurprisingly, the marine parks don't put that on their websites and promotional leaflets!

Unfortunately, swimming with wild dolphins and whales out in the sea is gaining in popularity across the world. Tour operators are always looking for new experiences to boost their profits, and are promoting this swimming in the wild as a responsible and ecologically sensitive experience. From Norway to Mexico, Portugal to Tonga, and the Azores to Tahiti, there are package holidays for tourists who can be taken out in boats and then dropped in the sea alongside a pod of dolphins, a gentle humpback whale, or a killer whale. All you have to do is swim. The more reputable companies insist that only 4 people are allowed in the water at any one time, but some companies are going to put more than 4 people in the sea at a time if it makes them more money. Already, campaigners and the World Cetacean Alliance (WCA) are calling for new guidelines. Using selfie sticks in the water alongside whales or dolphins is to be "discouraged". Group numbers will be restricted, distance restrictions will be put in place, and people will be encouraged to hold onto surface ropes. There will also be no swimming with whale calves and groups of dolphins with their young. This "activity" can compromise the welfare of cetaceans, by risking the lives of their young calves and potentially causing population numbers to fall. WCA guidance also suggests that boats carrying watchers and swimmers should not get within 300 metres of pods of dolphins and whales, because of the noise pollution from the boats. Then there is the disturbance from boats and swimmers for the whales and dolphins, who use up their energy reserves, when mothers and calves should be resting and nursing. Having to avoid swimmers in the sea puts tremendous stress on the poor creatures. Tourists may feel the benefits of swimming with dolphins and whales, but the feeling is not likely to be mutual. In reality, tourists are only having a negative impact on the very creatures they love.

In 1964, Morecambe's Marineland in the UK was built. It cost £200,000 to build and equip. It was welcomed as the first European "oceanarium", with dolphins, sea lions, and chimpanzees performing in shows for the public. The same year, "Flipper" was launched as a TV series in America. It reached UK television the following year. SeaWorld also opened its first "oceanarium" in 1964, in San Diego. It was the start of dolphin and killer whale performances, which became very popular forms of entertainment. The dolphin hunts were established in Taiji in 1969, as the Japanese discovered the lucrative business of supplying dolphins to these marine parks around the world. In the UK, in the 1970s, there were at least 36 dolphinariums and travelling dolphin shows with around 300 dolphins in captivity. But many people in the UK took heed of the "Save the Whale" movement, and their attention turned to dolphins in tanks. They began to picket the marine parks across the UK, and by the mid-1980s there were only 6 dolphinariums remaining. These were Knowsley, Whipsnade, Morecambe, Brighton, Windsor, and Flamingo Land. There was a killer whale at Windsor Safari Park, which was its main attraction. But due to concerns about the care of cetaceans at these marine parks by various animal and environmental groups, the Department of the Environment commissioned research to review the keeping of these animals in the UK. This led to recommendations for strict minimum requirements in the UK regarding pool size, feeding, water quality, and handling. The demise of the UK's dolphinariums came about very quickly, because the standards of care were so strict that they couldn't meet them, and 6 marine park closures followed. Windsor Safari Park closed on 25th October 1992, and was taken into receivership the next day.

Winnie, the killer whale at Windsor Safari Park spent 13 years there, with just a few dolphins in an adjacent pool to keep her company. Later, a male killer whale called Nemo was moved in, and he terrorised Winnie for over a year until he died of blood cancer. It is believed that Winnie was routinely starved in order to coerce her into performing. She was often depressed, and lay listlessly at the bottom of her shallow pool. She became extremely despondent. In 1991, she was imported to SeaWorld in Florida for breeding.

The dreadful business of exploiting whales and dolphins in the tourist trade can only cease if travel companies stopped promoting these hideous sea circuses and magical experiences. Tourists must stop buying tickets and booking package holidays to "swim" with dolphins and whales. It's a one-sided relationship, in which the balance of power is on the human side, and the marine animals get absolutely nothing in return but misery, pain, and hardship. So, keep this in mind, and understand how marine parks harm these sentient, intelligent, and family-based creatures, who can spiral into despondency and early death as soon as they go into captivity. We owe them much more than this.

Circuses

At the beginning of 2018, the Republic of Ireland introduced a ban on using wild animals in circuses. The Minister for Agriculture, Michael Creed, said the ban 'reflected a commitment to animal welfare. The use of wild animals for entertainment purposes in circuses can no longer be permitted. This is the general view of the public at large and a position I am happy to endorse.' At the end of May 2018, Scotland became the first country in the UK to announce a ban. The Welsh government has also made a firm commitment to ban wild animals in 2019. Finally, the government in England has pledged to put a legislative ban in place by January 2020. Public opinion polls have consistently remained overwhelmingly in favour of protecting wild animals, and in favour of acts enforcing means of protection for these creatures. The British Veterinary Association stated, 'The welfare needs of non-domesticated wild animals cannot be met within a travelling circus in terms of housing or being able to express normal behaviour.' These bans fall in line with more than 40 other countries in the world, including most of Europe, South America, and several Asian countries.

Many charities have been delighted with the outcome concerning bans and imminent bans. They have been campaigning to stop the suffering of wild animals in circuses for years. Why would anyone want to subject animals to a life in the circus – a life where animals are kept in cramped and basic temporary housing, transported from one end of the country to the other; a life of forced training periods and performances? Over the years, reports of brutality and abuse have been documented. There is nothing natural about noisy crowds, loud music, and loud bangs, and people coming round to try and pat animals and push them. There's no peace or quiet or restfulness. The poor animals can't socialise, and they can't display their natural behaviour. It's no wonder this leads to behavioural and health problems. For animals, a life in the circus is not one worth living.

One weak and silly argument that has been put forward by proponents of circuses, is that animals bred in captivity for performing, or for keeping in zoos, haven't come from the wild – and therefore it's acceptable to keep them in the aforementioned conditions. Why should any wild animal have to spend their life performing tricks in a circus, or pacing up and down a small enclosure? A wild animal is still a wild animal, even if they have been brought up in captivity for generations – captivity is not going to annihilate thousands of years of evolution. The tigers and lions in the circus are still the same as tigers and lions in the wild. They are not tame, and never will be. While the UK has abolished the practice of animals performing in circuses, we mustn't forget about what is still going on in other countries. Some of the most offensive acts with wild animals have been seen in Russian circuses. Russia has had a terrible reputation for cruelty whilst training wild animals, and for the unnatural conditions they are kept in. Endangered species like white rhinos and hippopotamuses have been used and forced to parade around the circus whilst carrying a man on their backs, being whipped if they do not obey. Tigers have been forced to jump over chained bears and monkeys, by force of the whip. Leopards and kangaroos have been made to have their photos taken with screaming children during circus intervals. This isn't entertainment; it's a horror show.

For a long time, there was no real government protection for circus animals in Russia. Animal circuses were regarded as fundamental to Russian's culture. Many Russians didn't see a problem with whipping or beating wild animals with sticks if they didn't do as they were told. But in 2010, Russia passed new legislation to improve animal welfare across the country. Vladimir Putin signed the bill called *On Responsible Treatment of Animals and Amendments to Certain Legislative Acts of the Russian Federation*. The Kremlin said the new law was based on "principles of humanity". It was originally introduced in 2010, and has taken eight years to finalise the act. Basically, it bans killing, baiting, and other forms of mistreatment of animals, including using wild animals in circus acts. It also covers the shooting and poisoning of stray dogs, sterilising, and vaccinating homeless animals, petting zoos in shopping malls, as well as animals in cages in bars and restaurants. Russia is certainly taking sizeable steps in the right direction for animal welfare.

Zoos and safari parks

There is certainly no shortage of zoos in the UK. So, which are considered the best ones? The most highly regarded zoos tend to be the largest, oldest, and most established, like London Zoo, Whipsnade Zoo, Chester Zoo, and Paignton Zoo. These have a history of participation in successful breeding programmes, and some of these zoos have returned animals back to the wild. They also have a reputation of being the most ethical. People tend to see zoos as a kind of tradition. After all, what family doesn't take its children to the zoo? It's considered a beneficial family activity, being away from television and computers, and out in the fresh air. Primary schools often include trips to local zoos as part of their curriculum. Children probably see it as a treat, doing something away from the classroom rather than schoolwork.

A zoo is a location where animals are kept in captivity and put on display for the paying public. In more recent years, they have dramatically changed, by making their animal enclosures more suitable for the animals they accommodate. Zoos also see themselves as playing a vital role in conservation, where they take part in breeding programmes to help endangered species in the wild. Education is seen as important for zoos. It is believed that when the public see real wild animals in zoos, it helps to create an emotional bond. This in turn encourages people to change their everyday behaviour, by helping them to understand that what they do has a direct impact on the plight of wildlife. It also encourages them to take an interest in conservation. On the research side, zoos operate and fund their own projects, as well as donating to larger projects – which are necessary to understanding the decline in some species. Zoos also help reintroduce wild animals back into the wild. But then ... do the paying public really see a visit to the zoo as something more than a day out? Perhaps they do, but only in a marginal sense. Their motivation for going to the zoo and paying for a ticket to get in, is generally for amusement. That's why zoos try hard to put on programmes for adults and children, to keep them occupied. In the past, they would provide camel and elephant rides, llama carts, pony traps, pony, and donkey rides in the UK. Overseas, you could find zebra rides and other exotic animal rides. Petting farms are popular with young children in the UK, and are arguably the easier and cheaper option, providing farm animals rather than wild animals.

Active learning opportunities can be provided with animal handler talks, direct contact with animals, animal demonstrations, and factual information based on various media techniques. But they can only be effective if they are seen to be a leisure experience. Zoos are competing with other leisure companies for visitors, and have evolved as credible destinations for tourists. Therefore, they need to meet visitor "expectations", to provide a fun and entertaining experience. Some zoos may provide animal walks with elephants, or help from the public with feeding some of the animals. But the emphasis is usually on customer satisfaction. As far as education goes, various studies have shown that visitors glean scant information about wild animals in zoos on their visits.

Conservation efforts and talks about breeding programmes and research could prove ineffectual if paying customers are not prepared to be educated. There is also little evidence that zoos are able to educate their visitors about the need for conservation, and the necessity and impact of any research programmes they are undertaking. This could imply that zoos are not actually very successful in creating any form of new interest or passion for wildlife and their habitats.

Whatever the size of the zoo, it is a costly business to run – probably far more expensive than the public realise. There are costs associated with the animals, including food, vet fees, bedding, staff wages, business rates and other direct overheads such as heating and water, rent, loans and mortgages, indirect costs like insurance, advertising, promotions, professional fees, upkeep and maintenance of the premises, VAT and other taxes, and the very important continuous investment on improvements to enclosures, new enclosures, visitor facilities such as cafes, toilets, play areas, entertainment, educational/conservation rooms, and car parking.

Zoos don't buy or sell animals. Since the 1970s, they have stopped taking animals from the wild and only "trade" or donate animals with other zoos. This in itself cuts out smugglers and poachers (who would take animals from the wild if there was a price on said animal's head) and all the associated brutality and cruelty that goes with poaching. Something like 45 per cent of zoos in the UK are privately owned, and about 90 per cent of the total revenue comes from ticket purchases at the gate. Chester Zoo is the UK's most popular zoo, and receives nearly £30 million pounds from ticket sales alone. There are some zoos that make a profit or cover their costs, but there are a number who are failing to survive or operate on a solvent basis.

There are a large variety of establishments that come under the description of a "zoo". They can be called animal farms, adventure parks, wildlife parks, zoo farms, zoo gardens, or even petting farms. In England, Wales, and Scotland you need a zoo licence from your local council if you "are displaying wild animals to the public for at least 7 days a year, in any place that is not a circus or a pet shop". There are various conditions you need to comply with, according to the gov.uk website:

- Help educate people about biodiversity;

- Be suitable for the types of animals you're keeping;

- Have a high standard of animal care;

- Do as much as possible to stop any animals escaping;

- Stop pests and vermin getting into the zoo.

You must also do at least one of the following:

- Conservation research or training;

- Share conservation information;

- Captive animal breeding;

- Help repopulate or reintroduce species into the wild.

Before you can get a licence, you'll need to tell your local council how you'll meet the above requirements. Then there will be a zoo inspection. The inspection may confer further conditions on a licence. After a licence is granted (renewable after 4 years and then ongoing every 6 years) there are regular inspections. It doesn't really sound too difficult to start a zoo, or at least not as difficult as it should be, provided you have enough initial cash to invest. If a zoo comes across hard times and is struggling, it can be several years before a zoo inspection team can be acquainted with what is going on. Therefore, animal suffering and death can go on for a long time without the local authorities being alerted. Surely, yearly checks are more appropriate? Some people are misguided into thinking that safari parks are more appropriate for wild animals than zoos, because they have more land to occupy. But they too can keep wild animals confined in restricted and small enclosures for up to 18 hours a day. Woburn Safari Park had a government zoo inspection report in 2010, which said, "The animals were very crowded and there was no provision for individual feeding or sleeping areas. There was no visible environmental enrichment. Some of the lions exhibited skin wounds and multiple scars of various age, some fresh, some healed." The investigation also uncovered the plight of large exotic turtles that had been kept allegedly in "temporary" tanks for months. West Midland Safari Park was shamed in 2012 for providing white lion cubs to a notorious circus animal trainer, who sent the cubs to a travelling circus in Japan.

The first drive-through safari park outside of Africa opened at Longleat, Wiltshire, in 1966. It was followed by Windsor Safari Park in 1969, but that closed in 1992. Later we had Woburn (1970), Knowsley (1971), and West Midland (1973), which are still operating along with Longleat at the present time. They all have the equivalent "family farmyard", "pet corners", "adventure playgrounds", boat and railway rides, and eateries. Again, the emphasis is really on a great day out, with lots of fun and amusement for the family.

Why should we keep zoos and safari parks open?

Even our best zoos and safari parks cannot compete with the environment of a wild animal. Not only are they unable to provide the amount of space a wild animal needs, but they usually can't provide a similar climate to what animals would have in their natural environment. Wild animals in captivity undergo excessive boredom and stress in confinement. They are seen as commodities, and traded for other wild animals across zoos and safari parks. If they are unlucky they can be "sold" to circuses and general public attractions, where they will have to perform to the public in other countries. Leaving family members and social groups, never to be reunited again, can be traumatic. Baby animals draw in paying visitors. Older animals don't have that pull, and they can be sold to run-down roadside zoos, animal dealers, animal auctions, or culled.

A government-funded study of elephants in zoos in the UK, discovered that 54% of elephants had behavioural problems during the daytime. An account of a single Asian elephant in a zoo in Alberta, Canada sums up the depressing life of a solitary animal. Words by Kristen Warfield:

"Every day for Lucy is mostly the same. She stands in her barren concrete enclosure, behind a glass wall, as visitors watch her slowly pace around. She has a tire hanging from the ceiling as a toy and no pool or mud bath to play in outside. And it's been over a decade since Lucy last saw another elephant. Lucy is 43 years old and has been at the zoo since she was taken from the wild in 1977 as a calf. She was alone for many years until the zoo brought in a young African elephant named Samantha for Lucy 'to mother' in 1989. Lucy and Samantha shared the same enclosure for 18 years. It was likely just as barren then – but they had each other. In 2007, the zoo sent Lucy's only friend away to North Carolina on a breeding loan. Samantha was never brought back."

Elephants are social creatures living in complex family groups in the wild. Why do zoos force these magnificent animals to live such a solitary life? It's not humane, and zoos shouldn't be allowed to keep animals in this way. Surely visitors to the zoo can see that this is an abnormal situation for an elephant to survive in? Lucy had many health issues. Asian elephants live in a hot climate, where the temperature is about 80 degrees Fahrenheit all year round. The temperature in Alberta during the winter can drop to -40 degrees Fahrenheit. In this case, there was a charity and supporters who wanted to pay for Lucy's transport to a sanctuary, where she would live for the rest of her days. But the zoo refused to let her go. The paying public wanted to see Lucy up close, and they were willing to pay a further fee to enter her indoor enclosure and "visit" her. Women went in holding babies, and families let toddlers run around when Lucy could have easily turned and become dangerous. It's all about making more money from the desolate situation that an elephant like Lucy has to endure.

Lions in zoos spend 48% of their time pacing up and down their enclosures. They are very popular in zoos. The vast majority are "hybrids", which means they are of "unknown subspecific status". They are bred in zoos to ensure a captive population of lions, and like a lot of other zoo animals have little or no value in conservation terms. They are kept in zoos because they are a favourite of the ticket-paying public. There are no clear conservational benefits of keeping lions in zoos. It is almost impossible to reintroduce lions back into the wild from zoos, because their natural instinct to hunt for food after being in captivity is impaired.

A Freedom for Animals study estimated that at least 7,500 animals and maybe as many as 200,000 animals are "surplus" at any one time in European zoos. If other zoos do not want these "surplus" wild animals, then The European Association of Zoos and Aquaria (EAZA) actively encourages zoos to cull them. Wild animals in zoos are regularly culled in the UK. In one zoo, a whole pack of wolves was culled because the social structure of the pack had broken down. Two wolf cubs and an adult female wolf were shot by a vet, who gave the reason as 'selective cull due to overcrowding and fighting in the pack.' In Germany, a zoo was prosecuted for culling three tiger cubs because they were hybrid and not purebred.

In 2014, a young male giraffe called Marius was shot by a vet at Copenhagen zoo, on the grounds that he couldn't be bred from, as his genes were "too common" – which would cause inbreeding. The 18-month-old giraffe was then publicly dissected in his enclosure in front of adults and children. His carcass was then fed to the zoo's lions, because he had been shot, rather than killed via lethal injection. This brought a negative response from across the world, and exposed the common phenomenon of culling zoo animals.

Over the years, plenty of UK zoos have been revealed as having conducted business with circuses. If the animals have a value, it may be seen as more productive to gain some financial reward rather than culling them. African countries in the last decade have been known to provide a range of young wild animals, including elephants, rhinos, lions, giraffes, cheetahs, zebras, and monkeys, to Asian countries. These countries include China and North Korea, who have an appetite for wildlife as they open up more and more tourist attractions. China contained wild animals like polar bears and beluga whales in glass cages and tanks in shopping malls, before their economy took a downturn. The idea of putting wild animals on show was to attract more customers. Yes, that's right – the sort who like to take selfies with the animals, by standing next to them on the other side of glass tanks and cages.

Welfare issues in zoos

Not all zoos in the UK are in great shape. *The Daily Mail* obtained 170 zoo inspection reports from local authorities using the Freedom of Information laws, and discovered that some zoos in England and Wales had serious problems: "At least 24 attractions appeared to have serious issues, while at least a further 17 were told they could only continue operating if they adhered to lengthy lists of conditions." Only one wildlife park had been refused a licence. After this newspaper article, some MPs called for an urgent review of the licensing laws, with a view to creating a national zoo inspectorate. Various issues were causing great concern, and below are some of the ones discovered from the veterinary reports obtained by *The Daily Mail*:

- One safari zoo had been allowed to keep its licence, even though nearly 500 animals had died there in under 4 years;

- A number of wild animals escaping because of "shoddy enclosures";

- Two chimps at one park died because their enclosure was accidentally overheated;

- A caiman (an alligatoroid crocodilian) was left outside in the winter and died;

- A peacock starved to death in isolation because the bird was forgotten about;

- Owls permanently tethered to perches;

- 8 Humboldt penguins killed overnight, allegedly by a fox who accessed their enclosure;

- 11 rainbow lorikeets accidentally killed by toxic bait, placed in their enclosure to catch rats;

- 2 lynx dead, one being shot after escaping, and the other down to a "handling error".

The list goes on. But one zoo in particular stands out for its dreadful record of animal welfare. Dubbed "Britain's Worst Zoo", it encountered nearly 500 animal deaths between 2013-2016. In June 2016, it was fined £255,000, after one of its female employees was killed by a Sumatran tiger. This tiger later died, and is included in the death toll of "nearly 500". The zoo also had an additional fine of £42,500 for health and safety law breaches, when a keeper fell from a ladder while preparing to feed big cats. Animals in the disgraceful death toll included: a jaguar chewing off one of its paws, a rhino crushed to death by its partner, a giraffe that was shot, and two snow leopard cubs found partially eaten in their enclosure. Then, in 2017, a lion died after being poisoned by barbiturates suspected to have come from contaminated meat. An MP called for a criminal probe into the death of the lion, and the RSPCA launched an investigation. Time will tell what future the animals in this zoo have, but it is a sad reflection on just how vulnerable wild animals are in captivity.

A few last words …

It's becoming more apparent that keeping wild animals in captivity has no benefit whatsoever for these animals, and little if any benefit to those who pay to see them. Animals in circuses are starting to become a distant past in some countries, but there are still many animals leading a cruel and perilous existence across the world at the hands of circus owners and trainers. Zoos and marine parks are forever looking for ways to increase their revenue. Many of them are corporate companies, where owners are shareholders. Decision making is normally based on making large profits, and the wild animals are nothing more than pawns in this process. The decision makers are too far removed from the cruelty and abuse of these animals, and as long as the company is making money for shareholders then they are not going to care. When animals die, they can be replaced. What every one of us can do in this world to help these creatures, is to stop buying tickets to these venues, stop buying tickets to circuses, and complain to your government. It's the governments who allow people to operate and continue the inhumane incarceration of wild animals. It's not going to change overnight, because it's not that simple to put the animals back in the wild. But it's a start, and everyone can participate in helping to make this happen.

WORLD ANIMAL PROTECTION   Website: www.worldanimalprotection.org.uk

Email: reception@worldanimalprotection.org   **Registered Charity No. 1081849**

"We are World Animal Protection

We end the needless suffering of animals.

We influence decision makers to put animals on the global agenda.

We help the world see how important animals are to all of us.

We inspire people to change animals' lives for the better.

We move the world to protect animals."

BORN FREE FOUNDATION

Website: www.bornfree.org.uk

Email: info@bornfree.org.uk

Registered Charity No. 1070906

"Since 1984, we have been working tirelessly to ensure that all wild animals, whether living in captivity or in the wild, are treated with compassion and respect. We work across the world to preserve and protect wildlife in its natural habitat – finding Compassionate Conservation solutions so that humans and wildlife can co-exist peacefully."

ANIMAL DEFENDERS INTERNATIONAL

Website: www.ad-international.org

Email: info@ad-international.org

Registered Company No 04741708

"Stop Circus Suffering is a global campaign by Animal Defenders International to end the suffering of animals in circuses. The campaign is built on the hard-hitting evidence collected by ADI Field Officers working undercover in the circus industry. ADI runs awareness campaigns, lobbies governments, municipalities and international bodies, and works with partner campaign organisations in different countries to spread the word and end this terrible and unnecessary suffering."

FREEDOM FOR ANIMALS

Website: www.freedomforanimals.org.uk

Email: office@freedomforanimals.org.uk

Registered Charity No 1124436

"We believe all animals should live free from exploitation, harm and captivity.

Freedom for Animals began as the Captive Animals' Protection Society in 1957 and is one of the UK's longest-running charities working to protect animals. Through a combination of undercover investigations, research, campaigns, grassroots activism, political lobbying and education, our work for animals focuses predominantly on issues affecting those individuals held captive in circuses, zoos and aquariums, as well as those used in the television and film industry, live animal displays and the exotic pet trade."

CHAPTER SEVEN
Hunting With Dogs in the UK

"If a man aspires towards a righteous life, his first act of abstinence is from injury to animals."

Albert Einstein

Hunting after the hunting ban

Since the *Hunting Act 2004* made hunting with dogs illegal in England and Wales, foxes are still being killed, along with deer and other wildlife across the countryside. Fox hunts appear to be going about their business as usual, hiding behind this great sham they have invented called "trail hunting". In reality, there appears to be little or no enforcement of the law. Since 1963, hunt saboteurs have been doing battle with the hunts to stop them chasing and killing foxes. Fourteen years after the ban came into force, the hunt saboteurs and monitors are still in the field tracking, disrupting, and monitoring hunts. This is because very little has changed since 2005 when the ban came into effect. A war is going on in the countryside, and it's becoming more perverted, with shocking footage of aggression, law breaking, and repulsive behaviour on one side, whilst the other side are being dealt deliberate and serious physical assaults because they are trying to defend our wildlife – the very same foxes, deer, hares, and mink that the legislation was passed to protect in 2004.

The hunting fraternity see hunting as a great British tradition, and are very proud of it. But what are they proud of? "Sport", "pursuit", or "tradition" falls well short of describing what hunting represents. Hunting with hounds is a cruel and barbaric pastime, of torture and painful death of wild animals. It needs to be abolished for good, by law, like cock fighting, bull baiting, dog fighting, badger baiting, and bear baiting. Yet even some of these hideous activities are still flourishing today. Badger baiting is widely condemned, yet the hunting fraternity are so proud of promoting this unlawful pastime as a wonderful British tradition. In order to make hunting sound practical and good for everyone, the hunting fraternity are now promoting hunting as "pest control", supporting farmers and the rural communities. It has nothing to do with controlling numbers, because wildlife doesn't necessarily need to be managed. The hunts appear to be happy to use whatever opportunities that may present themselves to further their upkeep of this tradition, even if it means breaking the law.

The police, on the other hand, appear reluctant to prosecute offenders of illegal hunting, even when video evidence is produced. Maybe the police feel their time would be better spent monitoring and dealing with other criminal activity, instead of saving foxes. What we do know is that the *Hunting Act 2004* itself is considered technically difficult to interpret and enforce. There have been convictions, but they appear to be falling in recent years. Cuts to police forces and funds for the National Wildlife Crime Unit mean there are very few resources for investigating and convicting wildlife crimes.

On the other hand, the hunt saboteurs and monitors have an incredibly difficult task in getting strong video evidence of the hunts contravening the law. Much of this can be deemed inadmissible if it does get to court. But even when the video evidence is strong, it doesn't guarantee a prosecution.

Many hunts operate on private land, and hunt saboteurs are often the victims of violence from hunt members, who accuse them of trespassing. There have been two deaths and countless serious injuries to hunt saboteurs over the decades, and it is claimed that the violence from hunt members has been escalating in recent years.

Since the ban came in, it seems the hunts are becoming more and more aggressive in their aim to keep their hunting traditions alive. For some time they were assured by certain politicians that there would be a repeal, and the ban would be overturned. But with mounting public pressure on the current government, the polls have shown that 85% of the public are in favour of keeping the ban on fox hunting. The Conservative government had little choice but to abandon their manifesto pledge to overturn the ban. There had been a passionate backlash amongst younger voters, with half saying they would not vote for a Tory candidate who supported overturning the ban. Fox hunting has become such a toxic issue that in the same polls 81% of people living in rural areas wanted to keep the ban.

The reality is that even without the ban, hunting was not likely to continue in the same vein as before. Regardless of comments made by the Countryside Alliance about the increase in the number of hunt members, interest in hunting foxes has reduced, and for some hunts this has resulted in a significant drop in membership. The trend is for hunts to amalgamate, because the countryside is shrinking. Hunts are facing other challenges too, in terms of income from membership, rising costs, and the anti-hunting fraternity. Some years ago, local farmers would support the hunts – the farmers' children would hunt, and their children too. But many farmers have given up farming in recent times, because they cannot make enough income. Economies of scale mean that farms are getting larger, and giving way to a more industrialised form of enterprise with larger mechanical machinery. The concern for killing foxes has become removed, because of the way the modern farmer deals with livestock. Most new house owners moving into countryside areas with lots of land are not interested in hunting, and many have forbidden hunts to cross their property. Add loss of land to the equation, thanks to road and motorway expansion, house building developments, and airport expansion across our rural areas, and the number of hunts across the country cannot sustain their activity due to so many restrictions as to where they can meet and hunt. Some hunts have disbanded, whilst other hunts have merged together.

Basically, the future for long term hunting with dogs looks bleak – it doesn't matter how hunters want to serve it up as a thriving sport. Yes, there may be an influx of professional people like stockbrokers, doctors, IT consultants, and lawyers who have moved to the countryside and like to hunt, but they barely have a connection or an affinity to the land. This can also be the case for horse riders moving into the area, many of whom are only interested in hacking along the lanes and participating in riding club competitions. It's true, the hunts have always had a strong link with the rural communities, holding fund raising and social events. There's the local point-to-point, pub quizzes, the hunt ball, horse and dog shows, and even village dances and country fairs. They often raise a decent amount of money for other charities, as well as for their hunt. But public opinion is against them, not just in towns and cities, but in rural areas too. This tide of opinion is getting stronger, thanks to social media, and will only grow whilst the hunts throw caution to the wind to defend something which has less and less meaning for people today. Especially as more people are now seeing hunting for what it is.

Hunting Act 2004

A long standing debate between hunters and anti-hunting campaigners who believed the hunting of foxes to be cruel and unnecessary, eventually led to a government inquiry into hunting with dogs in December 1999. It was named the Burns Inquiry, after the retired civil servant Lords Burns who chaired it. The inquiry accepted that hunting with dogs "seriously compromises" the welfare of the foxes, but was unable to state categorically whether or not hunting should be permanently banned in the UK. The government introduced an "options bill" allowing each House to decide on whether or not hunting should be banned or subject to license or self-regulation. Not surprisingly, most members of the House of Commons, in total 362 MPs, voted to ban the "sport". There were 154 MPs who voted not to ban hunting and the majority of these were Conservative. The House of Lords voted overwhelmingly for self-regulation, including Baroness Mallalieu, who is President of the Countryside Alliance. The few that voted to ban hunting included Baroness Fookes (involved with the RSPCA) and Lord Judd.

The government supported the House of Commons, which resulted in the *Hunting Act 2004* which was passed in November 2004. This law brought in the ban on hunting with dogs in England and Wales from 18th February 2005. Under the terms of the act, it is now "illegal to chase and/or kill wild mammals (other than rats or rabbits) with dogs." There are some special circumstances, called "exempt hunting" with dogs, providing certain conditions are fulfilled. Unfortunately, these are often abused, with hunts trying to exploit whatever opportunities they can to continue hunting as it was before the ban. The Scottish Parliament had already banned fox hunting in Scotland in 2002. In Northern Ireland, it is still legal.

There is no doubt in many peoples' minds that there is a severe enforcement problem with the act. It needs tightening up and clarifying in greater detail. Even if a dog does kill a fox, the law has to prove that the perpetrator fully intended for this to happen, in order for there to be any consequences. All the master of the hunt has to do is say that it was an accident. Being cynical, nearly every hunt would have meant it to happen if they could, but "didn't mean for it to happen" is a marvellous get out clause in court. Alternatively, if the fox gets clubbed to death, the clubber can always claim it was about to attack him. The excuses are rarely truthful, but they always work.

In a nutshell, you can't use dogs to hunt foxes, deer, hares, or mink. But you can use dogs to stalk and flush out "pests" – which includes hares, as long as they are shot and not killed by the dogs as soon as they are flushed out. Dogs can then be used to retrieve hares, after they have been shot. Rats and rabbits can still be hunted and killed by dogs. Drag hunting is acceptable because the dogs follow a synthetic scent laid down by a runner, which often contains aniseed, and so no animals are hunted. Hunts that previously chased foxes and deer, have invented "trail hunting" which supposedly follows a trail laid down by a rider on horseback, which is essentially fox urine. How confusing that must be for the dogs with the hunt – when they may very well pick up the scent of a live fox in the vicinity, and then head off, chase, and kill a real fox. It also begs the question as to where the hunts get their fox urine from. Anti-hunting campaigners have been complaining that the hunts have been flouting the law since February 2005. In some cases, it has been seen as an act of defiance, with some hunts publicly saying they will continue to hunt illegally despite the ban. They would prefer to go to prison than give up their bloodthirsty sport. This claim is endorsed by the fact that there were over 340 successful prosecutions related to the *Hunting Act 2004* prior to 2013, which makes this the most successful wildlife legislation in England and Wales. There would have been many more successful prosecutions if the ban had been more specific in its choice of words and meaning. The Master of Foxhounds Association (MFHA) claims on its website that "foxhunting" has only been restricted by the *Hunting Act 2004*. So, the hunts say they abide by the ban, but they actually work hard to exploit the law to its limits – which frustrates hunt saboteurs and anti-hunt monitors. Anti-hunting campaigners are adamant that anything the hunts claim to do in the light of the ban is merely a smokescreen, to enable them to continue hunting as they were before the ban was passed.

Fox hunting

The practice of hunting with trained "scent hounds" to chase and kill foxes originates back to 1534, when a Norfolk farmer tried catching foxes with his farm dogs. It wasn't until the eighteenth century that hunting foxes with hounds developed into the pursuit of fox hunting that we know today. In 1753, 18 year old Hugo Meynell (often referred to as the father of modern fox hunting) began hunting using a system. At his Quorndon Hall estate in North Leicestershire, he bred hunting dogs for their stamina, speed, and sharp scent. He hunted across Quorn country from 1753 to 1800, as "Master of the Quorn Hunt". Without doubt, he established a form of hunting which evolved into modern day fox hunting. Deer hunting was in decline because of the *Inclosure Acts* between 1750-1860. Deer had been bred in open fields and common land, but were now confined to smaller enclosures because of the demand for farming land. The Industrial Revolution further reduced the land for hunting deer, by adding roads, waterways, and railways. As a consequence, fox hunting became more popular, and continued to grow in popularity throughout the nineteenth century.

During WW1, fox hunting did decline, because many young men and horses were used in the war effort. A similar situation occurred during WW2, with hounds being reduced. But despite the banning of fox hunting with hounds in Germany during 1934, and in most other European countries from 1934 onwards, fox hunting in the UK continued to be popular well into the twentieth century. It was so popular that foxes were hunted to near extinction in England, and many had to be imported from Germany, Holland, and Sweden.

It would seem that fox hunting has polarised British society into two opposing groups – with sharply contrasting sets of opinions and beliefs. On the one hand, we have the anti-hunting group, who are adamant that fox hunting is barbaric and out of date, and that it has no place in modern society. On the other side, we have the pro-fox hunting group. who believe that hunting with hounds is "deep in our language and our culture". They argue that hunting is a central part of rural life and a revered British tradition. They claim some farmers have lost livestock to foxes, and see hunting as a much needed form of pest control. However, this has been refuted, because their claims have been seriously exaggerated. Besides, it has never really been a form of pest control or wildlife management. Books on the tradition of hunting with hounds have verified that hunts have always bred and kept foxes to later release to be hunted for "fun". These days the hunts like to bleat about the service they give, by keeping fox numbers under control, but these are baseless claims – because they haven't actually achieved this.

Fox hunts are very quick to point out that foxes need to be hunted to control their numbers, and that hunting them with hounds is the best way to catch and kill them. There has been evidence to show that foxes are territorial animals, and appear to self-regulate their numbers, providing that space and food availability is stable. During the foot and mouth disease outbreak in 2001, hunting was banned. Researchers observed this period, and found that the population of foxes did not increase. Hunts also like to claim that hunting foxes is natural, and that they play the role of wolves which are now extinct in the UK. What is "natural" about a pack of hounds that have been trained and adapted for hunting foxes, by chasing them to exhaustion? In the wild, foxes are predators. Wolves rarely caught and ate foxes, as they were not the natural prey of wolves. There is no humane way to kill a fox with a pack of hounds. The hunts even claim that foxes enjoy the chase, and that they often run in a circle instead of going to ground.

Of course, fox hunters will claim that fox hunting is good for the hounds too, because they enjoy the work and lead a good life. Yet after living in a pack of hunting animals, the hounds can rarely be found suitable homes, so they are shot. If they are too slow or too old, they are shot. It's estimated that thousands of hounds are shot or even clubbed to death each year. Many hounds are injured or die on busy roads, railway lines, and barbed wire fencing when out hunting. The hunt and their hounds also disrupt traffic, trample crops, frighten and kill livestock, overrun private property, injure or kill domestic pets, and can be a nuisance or distress to innocent parties. Not the good life for a hound that the hunt fraternity put forward, because the hounds have a life of a killing machine. It's also claimed that hunting with hounds improves the quality of the fox populations, because the healthiest are able to escape the hounds. That means that the foxes caught by the hounds are the ones who are weak, diseased and aged, leaving only healthy and sound foxes to survive. This claim isn't credible, especially when you consider that weak and sick foxes are hardly likely to have the stamina to be chased in the first place. Without the chase, there is no thrill for the hunters.

Cubbing

"Cubbing" is another hunting practice, that most people find rightfully appalling. Cubbing is the practice of setting young hounds on fox cubs, in order to teach the hounds how to hunt. The Countryside Alliance has renamed this practice "Autumn Hunting" in what might be an effort to make it sound more agreeable. These meets take place early in the morning at first light, or later in the morning, as the weeks pass into late September and October. They are often secretive, and those attending do their best to avoid drawing attention – it's believed that only the "hardcore" hunters attend these meetings. The theory is that from August to October, the hunt meets to train hounds. Before the ban, the main objective was to train young hounds to hunt foxes. After the ban, it was supposed to be "hound exercise". But like most activities to do with hunting, the hunts appear to flout the law, and "cubbing" appears to be carrying on as it was before the ban. Young hounds need to recognise fox scents, what foxes look like, and what they taste like. So, young and older hounds go out together as a pack, and are taken to various fox earths – where they encircle with riders on horses to drive out the vixen. The young hounds are then set on the cubs. If any cub tries to escape, the huntsmen and other riders on horses wave their arms, shout, and yell to persuade the cubs to go back towards the hounds in the circle. Basically, the best training for young hounds is to kill plenty of foxes. As the late 10th Duke of Beaufort wrote, in his published book called *Fox-Hunting*:

"The object of cub-hunting is to educate both young hounds and fox-cubs. As was said earlier, it is not until he has been hunted that the fox draws fully on his resources of sagacity and cunning so that he is able to provide a really good run...I try to be out cub-hunting as often as possible myself, and the ideal thing is for the Master to be out every day...Never lose sight of the fact that one really well-beaten cub killed fair and square is worth half a dozen fresh ones killed the moment they are found without hounds having to exert themselves in their task. It is essential that hounds should have their blood up and learn to be savage with their fox before he is killed."

Has fox hunting been a credible form of pest control?

Of course, fox hunters will put forward the theory that fox hunting is an effective form of wildlife management, and some would go as far as calling it "pest control" in the context of foxes. They will also claim that foxes need to be culled because they have no natural predators above them in the food chain. But do the foxes need to be culled when they provide such a good service by controlling the rabbit population? Pro-hunters will argue that foxes are a nuisance and "run amok" killing and maiming large numbers of chicken and lamb. It's true that foxes can steal chickens, but those who take care in fencing to secure their chicken pens say they rarely lose any. Many wildlife organisations give good information on how to protect chickens from foxes. Then there is the claim that foxes take lambs – this is likely to be a rare occurrence, as it is seldom reported. It is also difficult to distinguish between dog and fox predation on sheep, as they both attack by biting the throat. There are wildlife experts who say that culling wildlife hardly ever works. When foxes are killed, other foxes will move into their territory, or more cubs are born – to increase the numbers.

The *2000 Lord Burns Report* concluded that the "overall contribution of traditional fox hunting, within the overall total of control techniques involving dogs, is almost certainly insignificant in terms of management of the fox population as a whole." It is also estimated that 50% of the fox population are killed by cars in the UK each year, which is a large dent in their numbers. Given that the estimate for the number of adult foxes at the end of each winter is 258,000, and some 425,000 cubs are born each spring, the total number of registered hunts (before the ban) killed between 21,000 and 25,000 foxes. At least half of the foxes killed by the hunts were cubs, before the main hunting season began. The numbers killed by the hunts were in effect about 5%, and fairly insignificant. Since the ban, the fox population hasn't changed. Before the ban, when hunting with dogs was stopped during the foot-and-mouth crisis, research from Bristol University (Harris, 2002) gave evidence to show that the fox population didn't increase. In fact, foxes seem to be very good at self-regulating their numbers.

So, given this information, and the brutality and cruelty perpetrated by hunts, it could be suggested that the hunts serve no purpose in controlling the population of foxes. In fact, there is a large body of evidence that points to hunts capturing and raising fox cubs themselves, purely so they can release them for hunting. This isn't pest control, it's a blood sport. The Countryside Alliance claim that fox hunting is actually a form of conservation, and that fox hunters have a huge respect for foxes. This is a retort typical of members from pro-hunting organisations around the world. Everything their members kill, even by the most hideous and inhumane methods, always seems to be done "in the name of conservation".

Drag hunting vs trail hunting

Drag hunting has been around since the early 1800s. It was originally developed to test the speed and agility of the hounds. The version known as "hunting the clean boot" uses bloodhounds who follow the scent of a human. This is similar to a drag hunt with foxhounds, but the trail is usually shorter, and the bloodhounds are slower. The fox hounds have a human runner, who lays a trail by dipping a cloth in a natural scent mixed with aniseed or a chemical crystal mixed with water. This person then drags the cloth along the ground for the hounds to follow. The hounds are followed by the hunt on horseback, and the "trail" usually follows a pre-determined line, with plenty of obstacles to jump along the way. These are usually 3-6 miles long, and usually a minimum of three are organised for the day. Animal scents are not used, because the hounds are not chasing live quarry.

After the ban, the fox hunts came up with "trail hunting" as a way of keeping the hunting tradition and exercising the hounds. Someone on foot, horseback, or quad-bike (or a combination of all three) drags a cloth soaked in "an ethically sourced, quarry based scent" to make a trail for hounds to follow. But the scent is based on fox urine, and foxes are likely to reside in the area. Therefore, the hounds can easily pick up the scent of a real fox. When this happens, the huntsmen and other members of the hunt "stop the hounds as soon as they are made aware that the hounds are no longer following a trail that has been laid." But many hunt monitors and hunt saboteurs are sceptical. Whether the huntsmen cannot keep control of their hounds, or they are happy to let the hounds chase live quarry, the hounds will chase and catch a fox. There has been enough evidence on film to show this. Some believe that the hunts don't even bother going to the trouble of laying a trail, and that trail hunting was really designed as a false alibi to avoid prosecution for illegal hunting, when the hunts chase real foxes. This is probably the case for hare hunting too. There is strong evidence that fox hunts continue as normal. The question is, why are they allowed to get away with it?

The dark side of fox hunting

Considering fox hunting has been such an iconic image of British tradition, there may still be some people who will find it hard to learn that it is a very brutal and barbaric sport. People outside the fox hunting fraternity think that it is wrong to chase and kill foxes with a pack of hounds, whether it's for fun or for "conservational purposes". But the reality goes much deeper than that.

The ban on fox hunting was passed by the government on the grounds that hunting with a pack of dogs is cruel and inhumane. People who want to kill animals for fun are cruel and inhumane. Chasing vixens away from their cubs, so that young hounds can tear the cubs apart, is cruel and inhumane. One of the main problems is the amount of lies or untruths that fox hunters spread, in order to give their sport some sort of respectable front. They like to give a glowing account of why hunting foxes with a pack of hounds is the "most humane way" of killing a fox outright. But having chased a frightened animal with a pack of hounds, how can they believe the fox is killed instantly? When hounds catch a fox, they rip the creature to shreds, tossing it back and forth between them. By the time the huntsman dismounts and wades into a frenzy of excited hounds, he may only have pieces to pick up. It's not true that the hounds kill the fox with one swift bite to the back of the neck. There is no hound "singled" out by the pack to actually administer the fatal bite. Instead, it's a frenzy by many hounds, and they go for the fox's throat and belly – disembowelling the poor creature. If the fox goes to ground, the loathsome terriermen will use their dogs to find the fox, dig it out, and kill it. They may toss it to the hounds, or club it with their shovels.

The best way to find out about what goes on in fox hunting, is from those that have been former huntsmen and terriermen. People that have become disillusioned and disgusted with fox hunting have come forward to relay their experiences and encounters. Robert Churchward was one such man. He wrote his memoirs in a short booklet called *A Master of Hounds Speaks* published by the League Against Cruel Sports in the early 1980s. Having been involved with fox hunting, and later serving as a Master of Fox Hounds (MFH) for forty years, he was well-acquainted with the practice. He also stated that what he had written was 'correct in every detail' and made references to the vicious abuse he had received for making his views publicly known. Here is a description that he gave, of hounds killing a fox:

"At that moment the hounds rounded the side of the wood, in full cry, accompanied by staccato toots of the hunting horn and the beat of the horses' hooves. The fox had no chance; the leading hounds flung themselves on it, seizing whatever part of its body they could grip with their teeth, and in an instant there was a whirling melee. Sometimes one hound would bite another in its frenzy, and the noise was deafening.

On this occasion the huntsman and the whipper-in were able to grab the carcass of the fox before it had been mangled beyond all recognition and with a skilful twist of his knife the huntsman cut off the fox's bloodstained mask, which rolled down into a furrow. Next the pads and brush were chopped off. Then the huntsman took the rest of the carcass; as the hounds surged around him he threw it up, shouting "Tear 'im and eat'im!" In a few minutes the fox was obliterated; the hounds stopped snarling and quietened down."

In his short booklet, Churchward described a number of cowardly acts performed by the master and huntsmen towards foxes. These were fairly typical of what many a hunt supporter has let slip about their own experiences. They included:

- Foxes being unearthed and set upon by the hounds, instead of disposing of them humanely with a gun;

- Bagging foxes alive and keeping them for special hunts, where the hunters would slap them hard to terrify them, so the fox would sweat and urinate to let off a powerful smell for the hound. Then they would be tied up by their legs and dragged across fields to leave a scent;

- Cutting a fox's paws before it was released, to slow it down on the chase;

- Cubs being moved to another area for hunting if foxes were in short supply, to aid cubbing endeavours;

- Exaggerating the numbers of foxes to make it appear that they needed controlling, because of the damage done to poultry.

Another former huntsman, Clifford Pellow, spent 23 years working as a professional huntsman with a number of packs of fox hounds across England. As time went on, he became more and more outraged by the abuse of foxes ordered by the hunt masters. He was unable to stomach it any longer.

'In the end I got sick of all the gross cruelty and all the killing.'

Pellow protested and lost his job, and the master sued him for libel over comments he made in a Westminster press conference. A jury threw out the case. Meanwhile, Pellow was banished from the hunting fraternity. He gave many media interviews and became a supporter and campaigner for the League Against Cruel Sports. He wanted the country to know just how sadistic hunting with dogs was.

'Another time they dragged a fox across a couple of fields into a dry ditch before flinging the rope over a branch of a tree. They hoisted it up and then let it drop a bit so the hounds could bite it. They kept doing this to work the hounds up. In the end they just dropped it into the pack of hounds.'

Clifford Pellow spent his last years as an outspoken critic of the hunting world, able to use his knowledge to expose the cruelty of fox hunting. He died in 2016. Pellow is one of many who have disassociated themselves from hunting foxes, and though some have witnessed atrocities from the very heart of this so called "sport", there are many who still have a story to tell.

Deer hunting

Before the *Hunting Act 2004* came into being, there were three registered hunts which hunted red deer. They were the Devon and Somerset Staghounds, the Quantock Staghounds, and the Tiverton Staghounds – based in south west England. Before disbanding in 1997, the New Forest Buckhounds hunted male fallow deer, and there were at least two unregistered packs of buckhounds hunting roe deer in the south west of England.

Red deer were hunted in three time periods. Mature stags were hunted from the beginning of August to the end of October, hinds were hunted from November to the beginning of March, and young stags were hunted during March and April. A local deer expert called a "harbourer" would be employed by the hunt to select suitable stags for hunting. It would then be his job to locate the deer, and inform the huntsman about where to find the stag. The hunt would then take a pack of approximately ten hounds to the location, where the hounds would then separate the chosen stag from the rest of the herd. The hunt's "whipper-in" would then introduce the rest of the pack, say another twenty to thirty hounds, who would then pick up the scent. A harbourer wasn't used for selecting hinds, as it was very difficult to distinguish one from the other. The hunt would take the initial pack of experienced hounds, and encourage a hind to break away from the herd. The rest of the hounds would join in, and the whole pack would go after the single hind. Often, the hind would have last year's calf with her.

The chase could last an hour or less, or go on all day. The average time was about three hours, and the distance about nineteen kilometres. It was never a straightforward pursuit, as the deer would often get three or four kilometres ahead before slowing down. The hounds would sometimes lose the scent. After a series of these intermittent flights, the deer would either escape or stop running through exhaustion. At this point, a stag would stop and stand at bay. Then he would turn to face the hounds. On the other hand, hinds would stop and lay down. The hounds were trained not to attack the deer, but sometimes they did savage the deer quite brutally.

The idea was that the hounds would keep the deer at bay, until the huntsman and gun carrier arrived to kill it. Generally, the hunt had several hunt followers carrying firearms, and it was usually the nearest one to the deer who carried out the shooting. The deer would have its eyes on the hounds, making it easy for the gun carrier to shoot the deer with a single shot to the head. But sometimes the deer wasn't killed by the one bullet, and would try to flee again. The hounds would go after the wounded deer and bring it to bay, so that the gun carrier could take another shot to kill it.

The final ritual would be for the deer to be taken to a place where the hunt followers could gather round and watch the butchering and sharing of the carcass – this ritual was known as the "carve up". Various parts of the deer were shared out, with the heart going to the owner of the land where the deer was killed. The hunt supporters got a share of the liver and teeth, and hooves were given out as trophies. The offal was fed to the hounds, and what was left of the carcass was taken back to the hunt kennels, where the rest of it was butchered. The meat would be shared amongst the local farmers. The huntsman kept the skin and the head. If it was a stag head, then the master would keep it, and have it mounted.

So, why is deer hunting still going in England and Wales? It seems that stag hunts are taking advantage of several exemptions in the *Hunting Act 2004*. This law prohibits the pursuing of wild mammals with dogs, but allows animals to be flushed from cover by not more than two dogs. This is the activity that some stag hunts claim to be following, but some doing this have been prosecuted. Some stag hunts have successfully claimed the "observation and research" exemption, to avoid conviction, but many people consider this as an abuse of the Act. The bottom line is that they are hunting deer just like they did before the ban. The master will even change his jacket to a similar style and colour as his huntsmen, in order to keep a low profile. This activity has been recorded in numerous video clips, clearly showing the pursuit of the deer and the final kill.

Hare hunting

Hares are steeped in mystery and folklore, and are symbols of love, fertility, and prosperity. So, it may come as a surprise for many people that hare hunting and hare coursing, as well as hare shooting, were very popular sports before the ban on hare hunting and hare coursing in 2005. Unfortunately, there is a large amount of evidence to show that both banned sports are having a "revival". According to the Hare Preservation Trust, the number of brown hares in the UK has declined by 80% since the late 1880s, when the population of hares was estimated to be around 4 million. In the south west of England, the decline has been much worse, and the hare may even be extinct. Yet, there are about 16 hare hunting packs registered in this area. There should be an outcry that hares are still being hunted in the south west, and the government should be making legislation to protect hares. Modern agricultural methods are likely to be the main cause of this decline, but hunting and coursing, alongside shooting, have made a significant impact as well. To add to this, the hare is the only game species that doesn't have a closed season, which means it can be killed all year round. Organised shoots in East Anglia during February and March can kill 40% of the entire hare population. The breeding season starts in February, which means that a good number of leverets are left to starve or die in their mothers' wombs.

Both hunting and coursing are cruel and sadistic. There is nothing natural about hares being chased by a pack of hounds, or even two hounds, and then being ripped to pieces. Hares don't have the stamina of the hunting hounds, who will chase them until they are exhausted. Hares live above ground, and therefore don't seek refuge underground when they are being chased. In this day and age, it seems preposterous that hares are hunted with packs of dogs when they are not pests or food. Instead, they are killed merely for entertainment and fun.

Hare hunting involves a pack of scent hounds. There are more than 80 registered hunts that hunt hares in England and Wales. Packs of bassets and beagles are controlled by huntsmen on foot, and harriers by huntsmen on horses. The hunting season starts in late August, and lasts until March. Unfortunately these hunts have taken the same attitude as fox and deer hunts to the ban, and have defiantly continued to hunt hares. They use trail hunting as a guise to continue to hunt their quarry. This means they can claim they are hunting within the law, by "imitating" a hare hunt. Like fox hunting, they claim to lay a "trail" to mimic the running pattern of their quarry being fox or hare. This "trail", if it is laid, is inevitably laid in the same area that hares or foxes inhabit. Many hunts don't appear to keep websites, but on those that do it is interesting to read what they have to say about mimicking a hunt. On the Derbyshire, Nottinghamshire and Staffordshire Beagles' website, they have this to say about how they now hunt legally.

"Although the traditional quarry of beagles was the hare, we hunt within the law by laying a trail to stimulate the running pattern of a hare. This is a skilled job requiring considerable knowledge of the creature and its lifestyle. It is inevitable that live hares will be disturbed during hunting because natural and laid trails are often in the same area.

It is very important for the hare's sake not to interfere and call out if you see this happen, the hunt staff will deal with the situation and if they require help they will ask."

Basically, leave the hunting of the unfortunate hare to the hunt staff, and keep your nose out. It doesn't take a genius to see that the hunts are flagrantly defying the ban. Even if they were to leave "trails", the hounds have no way of knowing which ones have been put down by the hunt for them to follow, because they claim to use the scent of hares. Ridiculous, is a reasonable way to sum it up.

Hare coursing is where dogs such as greyhounds or lurchers pursue hares as a competitive sport. The aim is not to kill the hare, but to pit two dogs against each other in competition, to see which is the better one at chasing hares. Inevitably, the hares die, having been chased to exhaustion. There are rules, referees, and spectators who come to watch and wager bets. Some events have been on a large scale – like the Waterloo Cup – which used to attract thousands of spectators each year. But the *Hunting Act 2004* banned these events, and that included banning the spectating of them. After the ban, hare coursing almost disappeared, due to some high profile prosecutions. But in more recent years this practice appears to have made a comeback, despite the ban.

Mink hunting

Hunts first began to target mink, when otters became a protected species in 1978. The Masters of Mink Hounds Association (MMHA) was created, and some new mink packs were also formed. North American mink were introduced to the UK in 1928, to be farmed for their fur. Some were later released or escaped, and can now be found across the UK. There is a belief that as a non-native species mink are harmful to our river ecosystems, and should be considered a "pest". Generally, mink are replacing native predators such as otters, who have disappeared in many parts of the UK. Mink have a reputation for being voracious killers, and are blamed for the decline in the water vole population. They are also seen as a threat to many ground nesting birds. The debate still goes on about their impact on our native species, but they do come under the hunting ban. Therefore, it is illegal to hunt them with dogs.

Prior to the ban, the hunting season for mink ran from about April to early October, and the huntsmen and supporters would follow on foot. A pack of hounds would number 10-30, and they would be made up of otter hounds, foxhounds, and foxhound crosses. Most packs hunted by sight as much as by scent, and when a mink was sighted, the huntsman or hunt follower would "holloa" to let everyone know. The hunt would search along riverbanks, where the mink would have a stretch of territory for a mile or less along the river. If the mink took refuge in holes or under tree roots, the terriermen would be sent in to flush the mink out with terriers, spades, and sticks. Sometimes the mink would try to escape the hounds by running up trees. The hunt supporters would often step in and shake the tree branches, or throw stones at the mink to encourage it to come down. If the mink refused, then it could be humanely shot, but this was not often the case. Once the mink was caught it would be thrown live to the hounds to be killed or beaten to death by spades.

Like all other forms of hunting with dogs, the mink packs always claim to be hunting within the constraints of the law. There are approximately 17 registered and over 20 unregistered mink hunts in England. The usual approach to meets, is to insist they are only out to 'hunt rats' with the hounds. The packs maintain that their followers are still eager and enthusiastic, and that this is encouraging for the future of their sport. They believe there is much to be done to promote the benefits of mink hunting to the public – despite the ban, and the majority of people wising up to the sadistic nature of the practice.

The Countryside Alliance

The Countryside Alliance (CA) was formed in 1997 by the merger of the British Field Sports Association, the Countryside Business Group, and the Countryside Movement. It boasts a membership of 100,000 people, and many more supporters. The CA promotes itself as a rural campaign group, representing a cross section of the rural community including the "rural poor". It also believes it has wide cross-party political support, therefore affirming that it is a credible platform for campaigning on rural issues such as the closure of rural post offices, calling for better broadband connections for homes and businesses, and encouraging supermarkets to stock produce from British farms.

There is a wealth of information on how the CA was formed, their strategies, their defence of field sports, and how this is an organisation set up and financed by major landowners and the super wealthy. There appears to be a conviction within the organisation that because the overwhelming bulk of land ownership belongs to this elite group of landowners, they should be able to do whatever they want on their own property. So, to them, banning hunting with dogs is nonsense. While being part of the CA possibly allows them to defend their privileges and rights, it still doesn't give them the right to hunt with dogs. The majority of people in the UK are against hunting. For all the aggressive blogs, articles, and media put out by the CA, they still live in a democratic society. Loudly attacking wildlife supporting celebrities, wildlife NGOs, and anyone else who tries to protect the wildlife they enjoy killing seems to make those people more popular with the general public. The 85% of people in the UK who are against hunting are patronised by the CA, who claim that these people are being fed incorrect information about what the CA do and how they hunt.

The CA are very upfront on their website, saying the CA "continues to campaign for the future of hunting with hounds" and though it "supports all forms of legal hunting, we will continue to oppose what we believe is ultimately a bad piece of legislation." All pro-hunting organisations will protest in one way or another, claiming that what they are doing is enhancing the rural environment, and that opposing hunting is bad for rural economies – including animal welfare and a waste of police resources. Yet 81% of people in rural areas are against hunting. The CA wants to "liaise with the general public" to inform them how foxhunting and other forms of hunting can fit into "modern society". They also want "to dispel any misconceptions about foxhunting and combat mistruths spread about legal hunting activities." Perhaps they think that 85% of the population in England and Wales are all incapable of making up their own minds, from a wealth of information available to them, and therefore require CA propaganda to embrace a love of hunting with dogs. This is never going to happen. Despite the hunts and the CA claiming membership of hunts has increased since the ban, the evidence on the ground says different. There may be a handful of famous hunts that can still pull off a great show of pageantry on Boxing Day, but the smaller hunts face dwindling numbers and decreasing land areas on which to hunt. One serious area of alarm that has been raised by the general public, as well as by distinguished individuals in our society, concerns the recent cases of assault by huntsmen, terriermen, and "thugs" hired by the hunts. These assaults are targeted on hunt saboteurs and anti-hunt monitors, and some of them have been life threatening. But let's not forget the number of less serious assaults (not that these are acceptable in any circumstances) on women and men who are monitoring hunts during the season. There is a great deal of video evidence showing these altercations on the internet most weeks during the hunting season. Is this what the CA condones? The behaviour of some police forces when keeping an eye on the hunts, and their somewhat dismissive attitude to the blatant wrongdoings that go on, needs to be called to account too. The judiciary also need to be called to account in these matters, when giving out sentences which appear to be particularly lenient in some cases. More and more people seem to be complaining to their local MP, and this will hopefully help to get these issues debated at government level and brought to everyone's attention.

Another interesting aspect of the CA, is their accusation that hunt saboteurs and anti-hunt monitors are treating hunting as class war. But again, this isn't one sided. The hunting fraternity's behaviour and stance is to throw abuse and taunts against any hunt saboteurs and anti-hunt monitors, even when they are doing nothing to sabotage the hunt. There is a mass of video footage on the internet showing the tirade of class-based insults and derogatory taunts coming from huntsmen and their followers – language containing words like 'peasants', 'terrorists', 'scum', 'paedophiles', etc. as well as other demeaning phrases and threats. Class issues appear to be brought up by the hunting fraternity on a regular basis. Huntsmen have been filmed giving orders to the terriermen and hunt supporters to attack hunt saboteurs and anti-hunt monitors in the field, even when said monitors or saboteurs have said they are leaving and don't want trouble. This is hardly the behaviour of decent men and women, and it cannot be denied either – especially when film footage of some of these incidents is put out on local and national TV.

In response to the report that the Tory Prime Minister, Theresa May, had dropped plans for a vote on the future of hunting in Britain (despite it being pledged in her election manifesto), the CA responded by saying it was about "hatred of people". In other words, a conflict between social classes, the haves and the have-nots – the have-nots being the anti-hunting lobby. The CA seem unable to accept that there is growing support, especially amongst the younger members of society, for animal rights. People in the UK want their wildlife protected, to preserve it for future generations. They feel they have a responsibility. The opinion of the majority is that hunting wildlife with dogs is cruel and unnecessary, and that no one, from whatever class or background, should be allowed to kill wildlife for fun in the name of sport. It's fair to say that the CA, for all their rhetoric and claims that they speak for the countryside, are out of touch with the reality of public opinion. Repealing the *Hunting Act* would be political suicide, and a travesty of democracy for any government. The future of hunting is looking bleak.

League Against Cruel Sports

The League Against Cruel Sports (the League) was founded in 1924, and in the original charter it condemned fox-hunting, otter-hunting, stag-hunting, hare-hunting, and rabbit and hare-coursing, because they were organised forms of cruelty for pleasure. It's extremely depressing that nearly 100 years on, the League is still campaigning about the same issues. In the 1950s, it began investigating hunts and gathering evidence of cruelty. In the 1970s, the League increased its political campaigning. By the 1980s, it began undercover work, filming and photographing the cruelty inflicted on animals during hunts. Dog fighting and the abuse of badgers came under scrutiny, and after a landmark victory – successfully prosecuting badger baiters in the 1990s – the law was strengthened on the protection of badgers. In 2000, the League played a significant role in assisting the "Lord Burns Hunting Inquiry" which culminated with the *Hunting Act 2004* and a ban on hunting with dogs in England and Wales. Since then, the League has been busy exposing cruelty within many organisations, and has worked hard to prevent "a back-door attempt" to repeal the *Hunting Act*.

Even though a ban has been in place since February 2005, the League are still sending their monitors into the field to observe and record illegal hunting of foxes, deer, hares, and mink. The League knows all too well that it is a dangerous occupation for their team of trained investigators, which includes ex-police officers. They also have a hotline which allows anyone witnessing illegal activity/cruel sports to report it confidentially. They continue to educate the public, and policy makers too, in the media and via behind-the-scenes lobbying in Parliament.

The League directly protects wildlife on their sanctuaries and other land they own, which is in the region of about 3000 acres. No one is allowed to hunt or shoot animals on their land, because they hold the "sporting rights". Unfortunately, and outrageously so, it appears that their sanctuaries have come under attack. The League has a team to protect their borders, notably during the stag hunting season. As a long standing animal rights charity, the League has a reputation of being politically neutral, and are well respected by those defending animals.

Hunt Saboteurs Association

The Hunt Saboteurs Association (HSA) has been using direct action to stop fox hunting and protect wildlife in the UK since 1963. They use "non-violent direct action tactics", which include blowing hunting horns and whistles to confuse and misdirect hounds, laying false trails, and locking gates to aggravate and hinder the hunt. Now, with one of their greatest assets – the video camera – the sabs can film hunts actually breaking the law. Every season they save the lives of thousands of hunted animals up and down the country from "sportsmen" who kill for amusement. There are local hunt saboteur groups all over the UK. All of them are active at least once a week against hunts and shoots in their areas.

Violence has played a prominent part in hunting for decades. Two hunt sabs have been killed, and many sabs have had near fatal injuries inflicted on them, or have been hospitalised by huntsmen, terriermen, and hunt supporters. Before the hunting ban, the police came down on the side of the hunt, because it was a legal activity. Sabs were often seen as breaking the law relating to aggravated trespass. Since hunting with dogs is now illegal, you would think the sabs and the police would now be on the same side. But the law is very difficult to enforce, and the police are often seen as being indifferent to what the hunts are actually doing. The conflict between the hunts and the sabs continues, and there are still hundreds of sabs being injured. Certain hunts are renowned for being extremely violent, and have been known to attack sabs on sight. But the aim of the sabs, like the anti-hunt monitors, is to collect evidence of the illegal activity by the hunts on camera and video. The sabs also work at preventing the death of foxes by disrupting the hounds.

The hunts also spend time filming the sabs and the anti-hunt monitors. This gets confusing, as the hunt scream 'paedophiles stop filming the children', and the sabs and anti-hunt monitors deny the accusation as they shout back that they are doing no such thing, and are filming the adults and the hounds. Then the sabs and monitors are called 'terrorists' by the hunt, to sustain the idea that they are thugs and dangerous. But actually, the police have admitted the reality is that most arrests involving sabs are for "breach of the peace" or "aggravated trespass", which has nothing to do with violence. Usually these outrageous crimes consist of merely blowing a hunting horn in the field or spraying lemon oil in a wood. Yes, they dress all in black with boots and balaclavas to cover their faces, but there is a valid reason for doing so. The hunting community are ruthless in hunting the sabs down, to find out where they live. The sabs fear repercussions in their jobs and their homes if their identities are revealed. If the hunt finds out who they are, they will try to vilify them on social media, by accusing them of being paedophiles amongst other hideous things. Being a sab is not an easy life, but they do it because they are dedicated to saving the lives of our wild animals. The tide appears to be turning. With widespread public condemnation of how the hunts operate, the sabs are getting much more support and sympathy from the public than in the past.

The majority of sabs and anti-hunt monitors work in health care, shops, admin, finance, IT, teaching, and so on. Many are vegans, and outside of sabbing they live peaceful normal lives. They are not the class-obsessed violent thugs and villains that the CA or the press make out. They will be out in all weathers, ready to save the lives of foxes as well as birds and wildlife from murderous hunters. They are people who care, people who want to save wildlife. Surely that is better than hunting the animals down or shooting birds for pleasure?

A few last words …

Some argue that the *Hunting Act 2004* needs strengthening. Many of the issues surround compliance and enforcement, but that doesn't mean it hasn't been a success. There have been over 513 successful prosecutions under the *Hunting Act*. But whilst there are conceived loopholes, the hunts will work hard to exploit them, and wildlife will still be cruelly killed for "sport". It would be far better to have a total ban on hunting with dogs in the UK, and put an end to a tradition that is cruel and has no place in a modern society. Writing to your local MP, and urging them to support a total ban on hunting, will help wildlife to thrive in the UK.

LEAGUE AGAINST CRUEL SPORTS   *Website: www.league.org.uk*

Email: info@league.org.uk   *Registered Charity: England & Wales 1095234*

Scotland SC045533

The League believes "that a civilised country should not allow animals to be killed or cruelly treated purely for 'sport'. This is not a small problem – the number of animals involved in the UK is in millions every year. But we shall continue to act even if just one animal is killed for 'fun'".

RSPCA   Website: *www.rspca.org.uk*

www.rspca.org.uk/utilities/contactus   Registered Charity No: 219099

"We believe that chasing and killing live animals with dogs is barbaric, outdated and has no place in modern Britain."

HUMANE SOCIETY INTERNATIONAL   Website: http://www.hsi.org/world/
united_kingdom

Email: *info@hsiuk.org*
                                       Registered Charity No: 1098925

"Humane Society International/UK is a leading force for animal protection, with active campaigns to protect British wildlife including badgers and hares, to combat the slaughter of marine life, to reduce and replace animal use in scientific research and product testing, to expose and stop the sale of fur, and to reduce the number of animals suffering on farms."

BORN FREE FOUNDATION   Website: www.bornfree.org.uk

Email: info@bornfree.org.uk   Registered Charity No. 1070906

"Born Free is committed to protecting threatened species in their natural habitats and preventing animal suffering. Its purpose is to conserve and protect wild animals, natural habitats and functioning ecosystems in perpetuity, and to end any activities that exploit and negatively impact wild animals whether living in captivity or in the wild."

HOUNDS OFF   http://www.houndsoff.co.uk/

http://www.houndsoff.co.uk/contact-us   Not-for-Profit Organisation

"Hounds Off advises members of the public how to stop hunt trespass. Our advice is free and available to everyone. We help to stop illegal hunting activity on your property and unite others who feel the same."

KEEP THE BAN   *http://www.keeptheban.org.uk*

Email: info@keeptheban.org.uk   *Not-for-Profit Organisation*

"We are a very friendly bunch who's simply standing up for what's right."

"Our campaign has wrote to every MP in parliament, all 650, and has received numerous responses against the plans as well as finding the members who are planning to vote to repeal the ban."

ANIMAL DEFENDERS INTERNATIONAL   *http://www.ad-international.org/*
CONSERVATION

Email: info@ad-international.org   *Registered Company No: 04741708*

"Please help us keep this cruel blood sport in the past where it belongs."

HUNT SABOTEURS ASSOCIATION   *www.huntsabs.org.uk*

www.huntsabs.org.uk/index.php/get-involved   *Not-for-Profit Organisation*

"Protecting wildlife from bloodsport since 1963."

"The only organisation that works directly in the field to protect wildlife from the hunter."

CHAPTER EIGHT
Culling Badgers in the UK

"It is not helping the poor farmers. It is costing the taxpayers millions. The science has already been clear, but science no longer plays a part in the decision process."

Prof Tim Coulson of Oxford University, member of the Independent Expert Panel on the badger culling trials in 2013

Badgers in the UK

Badger persecution across Britain is as rife as it has ever been, and there are grounds to believe it is on the rise. How can this be happening when the badger is one of the most protected species of wildlife in the country? Unfortunately, it is also one of the most demonised animals by a broad cross section of society. If you have the courage to watch one of the videos showing evidence of badger baiting on the internet, you will see dogs tearing apart badgers, which squeal in pain as they are tossed about. The brave badger continues to fight the dogs to its death, experiencing the same terror and suffering a human would endure in similar circumstances. In the background, you will hear the cheering and encouragement of humans, with cruel boasts about the animals they are torturing. It's a horrendous crime, carried out for the sick pleasure of vicious criminals whose dogs may also suffer severe or fatal injuries. Sadly, it is estimated that thousands of people participate in this awful activity every year.

With their stocky build, black and white striped face, and grey fur, badgers are an iconic character in the British countryside. It's interesting that so many people in Britain will confess their love of badgers, when a large majority have only ever seen a dead badger at the side of the road. Does our appreciation for badgers come from growing up with badger characters in children's literature? Wonderful characters like Beatrix Potter's Tommy Brock, Kenneth Grahame's Mr Badger in *The Wind in the Willows*, and CS Lewis's Trufflehunter from Narnia, hiding from the wicked King in Prince Caspian, have all instilled badger love into society's heart. But what does society in general, know about badgers? Do we know that they are a social animal living in groups, in incredible underground living quarters called setts? Badgers will help each other when rearing their cubs. They have impeccable housekeeping habits, and can eat up to 200 worms a night as part of their staple diet, along with slugs, fruit, nuts, seeds, acorns, mice, rats, rabbits, frogs, birds' eggs, and hedgehogs. They can live for up to 14 years in the wild, but it's probably much less than that in reality. Being nocturnal creatures, they have a sharp sense of smell and good hearing to listen for danger.

Badgers are fairly widespread all over Britain, though more scarce in Scotland and some parts of northern and eastern England. South west England and Wales probably have the largest badger population. It's challenging to establish a firm estimation of badger numbers, given their nocturnal habits and living underground in setts. Most estimated population figures are based on the number of setts from sett surveys multiplied by the average number of badgers in a social group. Data for England and Wales in 2011-

2014 resulted in an estimated badger population of 485,000, compared to 250,000 from a survey done in the 1980s for England, Wales, and Scotland. Therefore, the data from the studies suggests that the badger population has doubled since the 1980s. It's also believed that Britain has approximately one quarter of the world's population of the European Badger or *Meles meles* as he is scientifically known. Badgers have been around for 300,000-400,000 years in Britain, having outlived their predators in this country such as lynx, bears, and wolves.

Being nocturnal, badgers are rarely seen in daylight. They are elusive in their natural habitat, because they spend the day in their underground tunnels or setts. They are social animals and live in family groups of around six badgers on average, but there can be as many as twenty badgers in a group. From spring to early autumn, badger activity may be seen in lanes and roads around dusk. Driving along a lane, you might suddenly see a badger trot out from under a hedge in front of your car and then amble along the middle of the lane. Doing your best to drive slowly behind the creature, the badger will turn its head to throw you a withering, disgruntled look, before disappearing into the hedge on the opposite side of the lane. For many people it's a special moment, seeing a badger in the wild. Some people encourage them to come into their gardens, by leaving food for them. They appear to be enigmatic creatures to say the least, but captivating and remarkable at the same time.

It's estimated that about one in five badgers die each year as a result of human activity. Up to 50,000 badgers are killed by vehicles on the road. Not all badgers are killed instantly, and many spend hours or days in agonising pain before they die. If you find an injured badger, you can safely transport it to a veterinary surgery during normal practice hours. Veterinary surgeons should treat the badger or any other small wild animal free of charge. This is worth knowing, because at the very least the veterinary surgeon can euthanise the poor badger and put it out of pain if the injuries are too severe. There are potentially up to 20,000 badgers killed via badger baiting or badger digging every year, and possibly thousands more – due to farmers, landowners, gamekeepers and hunts blocking badger setts, pouring slurry and diesel into setts, and setting snares to catch them. Then, of course, there are a very large number that have been killed by the "Badger Cull" in recent years, which is estimated to be in the region of 70,000 badgers since 2013.

Legislation for badgers

In 1835, the *Protection of Animals Act* determined bull, bear, and badger baiting to be unsporting, and made them illegal. But it did not outlaw the baiting of captive badgers, by setting dogs on then. The law was often ignored by the lower stratum of society in rural areas, who openly used the baits to gamble with money. Gentleman hunters looked down upon badger baiting, because in their eyes it was not a "sport". Today, it still isn't a sport – it's an inhuman deviation of senseless cruelty, watching a harmless animal get torn to pieces by dogs. Later, badger digging was seen as reputable, because it wasn't about badgers being set upon by dogs. Instead, trained terriers were sent down into badger setts, to corner a badger. A group of men would then listen, to locate where the terriers were, and dig down to find the badger. The "sport" ended when the badger was caught and put in a bag. It would then be either released or killed by the men. Apparently it was akin to shooting and ratting, where the badger had a fair chance of escaping. As the passion for breeding and training small terriers developed in the early twentieth century, digging clubs sprang up all over Britain. Rats and badgers were the ideal animals for their terriers to pursue, and it became a popular pastime across all social sections of society. But just how close was badger digging in relation to badger baiting? After all, both activities involved terriers, digging, and the capture of badgers.

In 1973, a campaign was successful in securing the *Protection of Badgers Act.* Unfortunately, it didn't go far enough. Though this gave badgers protection, it didn't give protection to their setts. The *Protection of Badgers Act 1992* protects badgers **and** their setts. It makes it illegal to wilfully capture, injure, or kill a wild badger, unless under licence from a statutory authority. It also makes it illegal to be in possession of a live or dead badger, and to destroy or obstruct access to an active badger sett. The *Hunting Act 2004* further banned fox hunters from blocking setts during the hunt. Since February 2005, hunts can only legally carry out "trail hunting".

What is badger baiting?

Over the centuries, hunting badgers for "sport" was carried out by farm workers and the rural poor rather than the landed gentry. It was considered not a gentleman's "sport", as the badger is a nocturnal animal and gentlemen are not prone to using shovels and digging down into badger setts at any time of day. They even considered badger baiting unfair, because the badger was never given a sporting chance to get away.

Badger baiting has been unlawful since 1835. So, why does it still go on today? It seems inconceivable that this level of animal cruelty is used as entertainment for a significant number of people in Britain. Harrowing evidence has been collected from various sources, which reveals that badger baiting is flourishing more than ever before. A BBC current affairs programme revealed that badger baiting is carried out each weekend across the country. They even discovered a website offering "badger baiting holidays" in Wales and southern Ireland. A getaway break for depraved and sick individuals to watch defenceless badgers being tortured and ultimately killed by fighting dogs – who would be interested in that? Apparently, thousands of people.

The financial rewards for people capturing or breeding badgers for baiting is about £700 per badger. There is a great demand for live badgers, with many events organised around the country. The programme estimated that up to 5,000 "baiters" are involved in organising badger baiting events. They have taken advantage of the internet and social media, to cultivate a new following for their clandestine activities. With the help of smart phones, they can upload perverted and sick images of baiting badgers with fighting dogs, instantly. They have even bred a new type of fighting dog called a bull lurcher, with the enormous jaws of a Pitbull dog, and the agility and height of a lurcher.

Once a badger sett is identified, the baiters send small terriers into the sett to find badgers. When the terriers find a badger, they bark, letting the baiters know they have found it. These days they fit the terriers with radio collars. A baiter stands on top of the sett with the receiver, and when the terrier is still he can pick up the signal and pinpoint accurately where they need to dig down. Once they pull the terrier and the badger out, they will use a spade or a bar to hit the badger and stun it. This allows them to get the badger into a bag, so they can take it away. But they may just throw the badger to the dogs, cheering and laughing as the badger is torn to pieces. The badger is a brave animal, and will fight on to his last breath – which only adds to the hunters' perverted sense of entertainment.

More often than not, the badger is taken to a private place for an organised baiting session, where it is put in an artificial sett. There is usually some sort of "tunnel", into which they can push a dog to go and get the badger. The badger will attack immediately, with its powerful jaw and claws. The dog will retaliate, and use its teeth to lock onto the badger. The owner of the dog will then pull the dog out by its tail, and separate the badger and the dog by using steel "badger tongs" on the badger. The badger is then pushed back into the sett, and the dog or another dog will go back down the "tunnel" to attack the badger. This is repeated over and over again, and is called "drawing the badger". All the time, the dogs and the badger are receiving horrific injuries. This practice is beyond depravity. The badger's fatality is guaranteed. The dogs can be critically injured. Baiters will deal with their own dogs' wounds and injuries themselves. Sometimes, they can find an unscrupulous vet to treat their best dogs.

It's not unusual for baiters to mutilate badgers, in order to stop them causing too many injuries to the dogs. Cutting the tendons in the back legs of a badger will help to slow the badger's movement. Pulling out teeth and claws, or filing them down, will cause less injury to the dogs. Baiters may resort to breaking limbs or jaws with a shovel. They have even been known to nail a badger's tail to the floor – nauseating brutality in the name of "sport", pleasure, and entertainment. It comes as no surprise that many badger baiters are known to be involved in many other dark and sinister criminal activities. Some may be just petty criminals, who operate on the edge of malevolent groups. In the main, people are too afraid of reporting badger baiting activities to the police, because many of the baiters have convictions for violence.

So, you might be wondering, why do people travel hundreds of miles to attend a badger baiting event? Many of them may be dedicated to following the performance of their favourite dog. Some people watch badger baiting for the perverse thrill and excitement they get from watching an animal fighting for its life. Some like attending for the betting; as much as £40,000 can change hands at an event. Women and children can attend with their husbands and fathers. Men, women, and even children have photos taken with dead badgers, to show their badger trophies to friends. It's very much a debauchery of sick pleasure and horrendous crime. The reality is so far removed from the lives of many people, that it can sometimes be hard to believe. But the perpetrators like to take videos and photos on their phones, which provide evidence of their sordid practices.

Prosecutions for badger baiting

Today there are an estimated 5000 people involved in badger baiting around the country, but most baits go undetected, and only a handful of prosecutions are successfully obtained. Back in 2007, only 30 people were prosecuted for offences under the *Protection of Badgers Act 1992*. By 2011, the number had risen to 58, though this was still a relatively low number of prosecutions. The Countryside Alliance was quick to respond, because many of the badger setts were connected to the hunts. They claimed that the RSPCA, League Against Cruel Sports, and other anti-hunting groups were using the *Badger Act* as a way of preventing hunts carrying out a legal activity. The Countryside Alliance also came out with their frequent defence concerning wildlife, which was that numbers of badgers were on the rise. In this case, they claimed that there were too many badgers in Britain, and therefore because there were so many badger setts it was easy to falsely accuse people of interfering with them. The RSPCA's response was that the reason for more successful prosecutions was based on an increase in reported incidents, improved technology such as CCTV cameras, and forensics tracking soil from spades. At the end of the day, the Countryside Alliance had no argument. They were committing unlawful and unacceptable atrocities against the UK's badger population. Currently, there is a maximum prison sentence of six months and a maximum £5000 fine, if a person is caught badger baiting. But there are flaws in this, because the erosion of budgets regarding wildlife crime means some police forces across the country are without any wildlife conservation officers (WCOs). On their websites, they state, "Most forces will have at least one WCO, whose role it is to carry out wildlife crime investigations." Back in 2017, a wildlife coalition warned that crimes against wildlife were going unpunished because reported crimes were not being recorded properly and assessed. In 2018, the first "annual wildlife crime report for England and Wales" was launched. At last, the public will be able to see the number of crimes against wild animals and birds recorded. So, reporting wildlife crime in the future will not be in vain, and will allow us to see what is going on in the countryside. The information for reporting wildlife crime on the National Wildlife Crime Unit website is currently as follows:

"If you witness a suspected wildlife crime in action call 999 immediately and ask for the police. For all other enquires call your local Police on 101. Alternatively, contact your local Police Force directly. You may also link directly to your local Police Force wildlife crime page via Wildlife Crime Links. Please note that at this time not all Police Forces have such pages and that the NWCU are not responsible for the content of any pages. If you wish to anonymously report a wildlife crime online please contact Crimestoppers.

NWCU has agreement that Crimestoppers will forward us your anonymous information.

When NWCU receive a Crimestoppers report we can ensure it is acted upon."

Landmark case involving badger baiting

Rare surveillance footage filmed by officers of the RSPCA's Special Operations Unit, culminated in the prosecution and sentencing of three men and a youth involved in badger baiting. It was described as a "landmark" case and welcomed by The League of Cruel Sports and many other charities and individuals who sought protection for British wildlife. The three adult defendants were caught red-handed, deliberately using dogs to attack a badger. Images of fake setts, and skulls of foxes and badgers, were also used as evidence in court.

One of the defendants was imprisoned immediately for 22 weeks and placed under close supervision for a 12-month period. He was fined the maximum £5000, and disqualified from keeping dogs for an eight year period. He was also reported as having been a huntsman for 32 years. The League of Cruel Sports stated that it came as no surprise that a huntsman had been engaged in barbaric cruelty to animals. Various groups calling for the disbandment of the relevant hunt, and relocation of their hounds, were in agreement that this individual should have no further involvement in terrorising and killing wildlife.

Another of the defendants was given an immediate prison sentence of 20 weeks, and was also placed under close supervision for a year. He was fined £600, a victim surcharge of £150, and was disqualified from keeping dogs for an eight-year period. The third defendant was given a 10-week prison sentence (suspended for 12 months), and was disqualified from keeping dogs for a four-year period. He was also ordered to perform 150 hours of unpaid work, pay costs of £500, and a victim surcharge of £150. The 17-year-old youth was given a 10 month referral order, a four-year ban on keeping dogs, and ordered to pay costs of £200 and a victim surcharge of £20.

Three days after the offence, the police and the RSPCA seized 23 dogs and two foxes in cages from the farm where the badger baiting was carried out. The foxes were terrified, and suffering from being kept so close to the dogs. It was thought that these foxes had been caught with the intention of setting the dogs on them at a later date. A further eight dogs were seized from another associated address. While the defendants contested the case fiercely, the evidence was overwhelming. The judge was adamant that, 'This was a deliberate and planned venture to cause suffering to an animal.' All of the defendants were charged under the *Protection of Badgers Act 1992* and *Animal Welfare Act 2006*.

Badger culling pre-2012

In 1960, Britain was declared free of bovine TB (bTB), as it was widely believed that bTB had been brought under control. This was seen as one of the greatest achievements in post-war British agriculture. Herd testing frequency was relaxed, and in 1979 less than 0.5 per cent of the national herd was infected. The infected herds were geographically concentrated in two areas, in the southwest of England. In 1971, a dead badger infected with bTB was discovered in Gloucestershire. This led to badger-culling commencing in 1973. This was the same year that the *Protection of Badgers Act* was introduced to protect badgers from baiting, by prohibiting "the taking, injuring, or killing of badgers". Licences were initially given to farmers under the *Badger Act* for cage trapping or free shooting badgers. There were concerns about the welfare of badgers being shot by farmers, and in 1975 the Ministry of Agriculture, Fisheries and Farming (MAFF) took over the culling of badgers. MAFF culled badgers by gassing them, putting cyanide in their setts, between 1975 and 1981. There was much public opposition to this, and the government policy was widely criticised in both the national press and scientific publications. Gassing innocent creatures revived the memory of the Nazi holocaust, and kindled many ardent responses to this terrible deed. It had not been proved that badgers were responsible for the ongoing outbreaks of bTB in cattle herds, and thus the government ultimately had to give in to public pressure and call a moratorium on gassing badgers. These concerns about the culling of badgers resulted in a number of studies and reports on the welfare of badgers.

During 1980, a review by Lord Zuckerman, at the time President of the London Zoological Society, found that badgers were a reservoir of bTB infection and proposed a "clean ring" theory. This involved sampling badgers around infected farms and culling a whole sett if badgers were found to be positive. Further adjacent setts would then be tested and culled if also positive, until no more infected badgers were found. The process would continue for six months, to maintain a "clear ring" around the farm. Lord Zuckerman's recommendations included greater openness and called for more scientific research. The Nature Conservancy Council were frustrated by the Ministry of Agriculture's refusal to consult properly. It was secretive and had disregard for scientific evidence. The blame for this at the time was laid at the door of the National Farmers' Union and the Country Landowners Association (CLA), now known as The Country Land and Business Association (CLA). From what can be gleaned from the media today, it seems these were the same grievances that had first been experienced nearly 30 years ago, and have been ongoing throughout the history of badger culling.

In the words of the journalist Matthew Kelly: "Looking back is to be struck by the rapidity with which the farming community latched onto the need to kill badgers, the ad-hoc and unsystematic nature of the government's response and the deeply troubled relationship between scientific understanding and policy formation".

Part of the problem appears to be with farmers and politicians, who have been unwavering in laying the blame on badgers.

The introduction of the *Protection of Badgers Act 1992* consolidated all previous legislation including the amended *Badgers Act 1973* and the *Badgers Act 1991*. In a nutshell, the law bans people from injuring, killing, or taking badgers, or disturbing their setts. The outcome of this is, theoretically, a high level of protection for badgers in the wild. Or is it? The reality is that badger baiting has continued, and appears to be more popular than ever before. Hunts, who are not supposed to be hunting, are still blocking up setts to stop foxes escaping underground, and terriermen are still digging for badgers. Hunt sabs are filming these unlawful acts every week, and yet the police are taking no notice of the laws being broken. To make it worse, licenses are being issued for people to go out and kill thousands of badgers in the name of "badger culls", with financial rewards for those who carry out the culling. Yet we still don't know if badgers are actually spreading bTB across cattle herds. Badgers are acknowledged as a reservoir for bTB, but the actual contribution of badgers on the incidence and spread of the disease is hard to quantify. The disease is very patchy in various areas, and can also be passed from cows to badgers and between cows in the same herd. Even after five decades of debate, there is still uncertainty. Scientific research and culls have failed to provide an answer as to what proportion, if any, of cattle bTB cases are caused by badgers. Farmers who are pro-cull appear to be unshakeable in their view that reducing badger numbers will reduce bTB in the environment.

From 1998-2006, the Randomised Badger Culling Trial (RBCT) took place in England. This was a large-scale field trial, also known as the Krebs Trial. Its mission was to assess the impact of culling badgers on the incidence of bTB in cattle, and was overseen by the Independent Scientific Group (ISG). It also looked into the effectiveness of strategies in reducing the risk of bTB in cattle. The RBCT represented ten years of research, funded by nearly £50 million of taxpayers' money. In the final report on cattle bTB, published in 2007, the ISG concluded "that badger culling was unlikely to contribute positively, or cost effectively, to the control of cattle bTB in Britain." Following the findings of the RBCT, the Labour government in 2008 decided not to put forward a badger cull to control bTB in cattle. However, following the 2010 election, the Coalition government agreed that a badger cull would be on the agenda as part of bTB control measures. Where was the science behind that decision?

Badger culling 2012-2018

In late December 2011, Caroline Spelman, a Conservative MP and Secretary of State for Environment, Food and Rural Affairs, announced that there was no alternative but to approve the pilot badger culls – because of the number of cattle afflicted with bTB. Peter Kendall, the president of the National Farmers Union (NFU), agreed with the cull proposals. As head of an organisation who sees itself as "the voice of British farming", he said, 'Today is another massive step forward in achieving our end goal of a healthy countryside – both for badgers and for cattle. The most recent science shows badger controls are absolutely necessary, together with cattle controls, to get on top of TB.' But scientists voiced strong disagreement. Rosie Woodruffe, a badger ecologist at the Institute of Zoology in London, who was involved for ten years with the Independent Scientific Group on Tuberculosis in Cattle at DEFRA, disagreed. Her opinion was that, at best, it would only achieve a 16 per cent reduction in cattle TB, would cost farmers more money, and would make cattle TB worse than it already was. Lord Krebs, the former scientific adviser and architect of the 10 year trial, said the results proved that badger culls were not effective in controlling bTB. He said, 'You cull extensively for at least four years and you will have a net benefit of reducing TB cattle of 12-16 per cent. So you leave 85 per cent of the problem still there, having gone to a huge amount of trouble to kill a huge amount of badgers. It doesn't seem an effective way of controlling the disease.'

So, on the one hand you had the farming community, the NFU, and the politicians, all firmly behind the pilot culls. On the other hand, you had the scientists and researchers, who were adamant that it was a waste of time, and wildlife campaigners who were up in arms at a potential huge loss of badgers in the wild. Then there was the cost of it all to taxpayers and farmers. Lord Krebs suggested a better option would be to try and develop a vaccine for the future, and in the short term put in biosecurity measures to keep cattle away from badgers. In July 2012, a legal bid by The Badger Trust to stop the proposed badger cull in England failed at the High Court. It was argued by the Trust that the cull was illegal, and more than likely would make disease amongst cattle worse. The government moved forward with the badger cull trials regardless. In October 2012, the Secretary of State for the Environment, Owen Paterson, declared the cull trials would be postponed until 2013, due to bad weather in the summer, and policing constraints.

In the autumn of 2013, the controversial badger culling trials were introduced in Gloucestershire and Somerset, as a means of testing the "effectiveness, humaneness and safety of controlled shooting". There was also the provision of cages to trap badgers, but this was intended to be on a small scale. DEFRA appointed an Independent Expert Panel (IEP), who discovered that cages had been introduced, on a large scale, within just three days of the trials beginning – and this continued throughout the duration. This made the evaluation of the effectiveness of controlled shooting very difficult to assess, because badgers trapped in cages could not be shot as unrestrained animals. Basically, the premise the IEP were brought in to evaluate – which was the effectiveness of controlled shooting – was thwarted by the number of cages that were used. Resources and effort were being diverted from shooting to trapping. The unreliability of data regarding contractor efforts and the locations where badgers were shot, was cause for concern. It meant that elements of important analysis were not possible, and thus were skipped altogether.

The IEP referred to various changes that were made during the culls, that had not been agreed before the culls started. With regards to humaneness, some contractors were shooting badgers at ranges in excess of Best Practice Guidance. Observers were also reporting that some contractors were shooting at badgers that were too close to cover or setts. This reduced the opportunity to take a second shot at a wounded badger, before it went underground. The IEP recommended that if controlled shooting was to be considered for any future culls, the overall standard of competence of contractors in the field needed be raised. A small number of contractors were unwilling to be accompanied by observers, and it was made clear that such evasive action by contractors was unacceptable. Cull companies and Natural England as the licensing authority were advised to have more robust systems in place – systems which would allow them to monitor contractors' performances, in order to identify inefficient individuals quickly and remove them from the cull. It seems the Best Practice assessment used before the cull did not weed out those who were poor shots in the field.

There was also a lot of criticism towards the contractors with regards to basic safety conditions. There were occasions when contractors were surprised by protesters almost immediately after shooting, because they had not cleared the shooting area sufficiently well. A pre-condition to granting the contractors with firearms certificates, was that they would not attempt to shoot if protesters or members of the public were in the vicinity. Whilst there were no serious incidents, the police recorded a number of "near misses". Gloucestershire police were also concerned that in addition to these near misses, there were a number of confrontational incidents between the cull operators and the protesters. The police reported that the contractors were not experienced when dealing with the protesters, who were well prepared and knowledgeable in regard to legal matters. Also, there were some accounts from contractors which conflicted directly with video evidence of incidents.

Natural England reported that some contractors did not adhere to Best Practice Guidance relating to the handling of badger carcasses and biosecurity. They also suggested that contractors didn't always act in a professional and competent manner. This was of concern to the IEP, who suggested that improvements needed to be made before the next cull. Concerns were also raised by the IEP about humaneness with regards to the badgers that were killed. Interestingly, the IEP members were not invited back to the second round of badger culling trials in 2014. The Badger Trust went to court over this, arguing that it was crucial to ensure an IEP was put in place for the next round of trials. Campaigners said the government was acting unlawfully, and that it would be unacceptable to go ahead without an IEP monitoring and ensuring the badgers were being killed in a humane way. The three judges dismissed the case, and DEFRA went ahead without an IEP in place.

On 27 August 2013, the badger cull trials commenced. After the initial six-week period, the culls in both areas were extended by 2 more weeks. This was due to the failure to cull 70% of the badgers required, as set out in the government badger control policy. At the end of November, it was estimated that 65% of the badgers were culled in the Somerset trial, and just under 40% of the badgers in the Gloucestershire trial, totalling 1,861 badgers removed. In April 2014, Owen Paterson announced that the cull trials would continue in the same areas as before, and would not extend to areas where new outbreaks had been reported. Culling began in September 2014. The target for culling badgers in Gloucestershire was 615-1,091, and for Somerset the target was 316-785. The minimum target for culled badgers was met in Somerset, but not in Gloucestershire. A total of 615 badgers were removed from the trial areas. Opposition to the badger culls led to a great deal of press coverage from the RSPCA, Wildlife Trusts, Badger Trust, and League of Cruel Sports. Protesters were out in numbers trying to disrupt the culls in both 2013 and 2014 trials. At night they were out looking for injured badgers walking along public footpaths in the dark. Anti-cull saboteurs tried to interrupt shooting, and released any trapped badgers in cages. The NFU was granted a court injunction to prevent certain activities by protesters, because of claims that farmers involved in the culls were being intimidated and harassed. The British Veterinary Association (BVA) raised concerns about the controlled shooting of badgers, citing problems with efficiency and humaneness. They called for all badgers to be trapped and shot going forward, in any future culls. Three areas were licenced for the 2015 cull, as Gloucestershire and Somerset were joined by Dorset. The licences allowed free shooting of badgers, and the trapping of badgers before shooting. Two other areas in Devon and Herefordshire had their cull applications turned down by Natural England. The three areas succeeded in culling their target numbers of badgers to be removed. In 2016, seven new areas were added to the three existing areas of 2015. These were in Cornwall, Devon, Dorset, Gloucestershire, and Herefordshire. All ten cull areas achieved their minimum cull targets. The total of 10,886 badgers culled was made up of 5,219 badgers trapped and shot, and 5,672 who were shot. Eleven new culling areas across Cheshire, Devon, Dorset, Somerset, and Wiltshire were added in 2017. A total of 19,274 badgers culled was made up of 7,636 badgers trapped and shot, and 11,638 who were shot. No details of the locations were made public.

In 2018, more than 32,000 badgers were killed. Another 11 areas were added to the cull, making a total of 32 cull areas. Companies limited by guarantee were being formed by farmers and landowners, for managing the badger culls. Independent scientists accused the government of making up targets and optimistic statements based on unreliable data. As yet, there has been no official report giving details on the 2018 badger cull. The government claimed the culls had been successful and effective, and that bTB was being reduced in cattle.

Tale of the hounds – was it a Kimblewick Hunt cover up?

The Kimblewick Hunt came together in 2002, by amalgamating the Vale of Aylesbury with the Garth and South Berks, which was previously the Garth, the South Berks, the Old Berkeley, the South Oxfordshire, and Hertfordshire Hunts. The hunt boasts that its hounds are taken across six counties of England. Their hunt kennels are at Kimblewick, a hamlet within a parish of the Wycombe district, in Buckinghamshire. In December 2016, the Kimblewick Hunt's pack of hounds were found to be infected with bTB. Of 164 hounds tested, 97 had evidence of being bTB infected, and these dogs were removed and euthanised. A kennel worker also tested positive for the disease, as well as 2 out of 19 pet dogs associated with the pack of hounds. The hunt kennels were said to be overcrowded, and were described as "suboptimal", meaning the hounds were kept in unhygienic, overcrowded, and dilapidated conditions, which could be a breeding ground for disease. Following this news, the RSPCA called for the regulation of hunt kennels, which are exempt as they are not considered a commercial enterprise. This is patently absurd. Why should hunt kennels not be inspected and licensed, just like any other kennels, in the name of animal welfare?

The University of Edinburgh released a report into the outbreak of bTB at the Kimblewick kennels. The report suggested there were two plausible reasons why the hounds could have been infected by bTB. The first reason could have been based on the hounds visiting other hunt kennels for breeding purposes, or the practise of loaning hounds (which is apparently commonplace). Hounds are not tested for bTB before pre-movement or post-movement to other kennels. The second reason is the feeding of "fallen stock" to the hounds. This refers to livestock that has died. Hunts have traditionally offered a service to farmers to take their fallen stock, which is then fed to their hounds. It saves money, for both the farmers and the hunts. Apparently, it has been known for many years that fallen stock can contain disease, which is then passed on to the hounds and even to the kennel staff. It is worth mentioning that there is a Council of Hunting Associations Code of Practice, consisting of 27 pages (updated December 2014), which goes into detail about how hunts should look after the hounds, in light of the *Animal Welfare Act 2006*. Under 7.5 Infectious and Contagious diseases it states, "Nowadays there are only two serious diseases that may present a problem in packs of hounds – kennel cough and mange." Perhaps the Council of Hunting Associations should revise their code of practice and give advice on another serious disease – bovine tuberculosis. The Animal & Plant Health Agency (APHA), an executive agency sponsored by DEFRA, last updated its guidance on bovine tuberculosis (TB) in cats and dogs with suspected or confirmed bovine TB infection, in March 2017. The guidance clearly states that your infected cat or dog could pass on the infection to humans and other animals, if they come in contact with your pet. Well, hounds are dogs. If they are infected then they also could pass the infection to many farm animals, as well as pets, when they are taken out for exercise or hunting.

It is certainly credible to argue that the hounds belonging to the Kimblewick Hunt, of which a very large number had bTB, could have been responsible for spreading the disease across farmland. The hunt takes the hounds across a large number of farms in six different counties, and this should without a doubt have been a concern. But there didn't appear to be a worried response from DEFRA. Basically, they weren't interested. Official figures showed there had been 55 new cattle herds infected with bTB in the area covered by the Kimblewick Hunt, four months after the hunt dealt with their hound infections. This had more than doubled the previous number of 35, as there were now 90 cattle herds infected with bTB in the area covered by the Kimblewick Hunt. The Prion Interest Group's veterinary scientists, independent scientists, and animal welfare societies, were outraged. They were very vocal with their concern about this information. They made several Freedom of Information (FOI) requests to DEFRA, which appeared to be obstructed by DEFRA. This led to accusations that information was probably being withheld and DEFRA were being "secretive". It took quite some time before the correct facts were revealed. A spokesperson from APHA said that bTB is not a 'notifiable disease in dogs', and therefore they were unable to verify how many hounds had been put down. APHA also said they had 'offered advice to the hunt kennels on options for managing this case', but whether the hunt took the advice or not, we don't know.

Lord Gardiner of Kimble served as Parliamentary Under Secretary of State at DEFRA from 17 July 2016 to January 2018. He had been Director of Political Affairs at the Countryside Alliance between 1995 and 2004, and then Deputy Chief Executive between 2004 and 2010. He was also an honorary member of the Kimblewick Hunt. When the Kimblewick cover-up became public, anti-hunting campaigners were quick to point the finger at him. DEFRA was adamant that they took biosecurity and animal welfare extremely seriously, even though they expected the hunts to put in place their own regulations to protect people and animals from any risk of disease from their hounds. They claimed that bTB in dogs was extremely rare, and that there was no evidence of hunting dogs spreading it to farm animals. Yet it has been known for many years that fallen stock contains diseases, which are passed on to dogs when they eat the body. Scientists say that these diseases are then spread around the countryside, as hounds defecate and urinate whilst running across farmland. Vet Dr Iain McGill, Director of the Prion Interest Group (PIG) and former Ministry of Agriculture, Fisheries and Food (MAFF) and Zoological Society of London (ZSL), scientist, and League Against Cruel Sports, called for all hunting to be suspended until an independent inquiry can verify if hunting hounds are spreading bTB. A veterinary research group told the media that there is a great deal more evidence to demonstrate that hunt hounds are responsible for spreading bTB, than there is for badgers. They suggested that the government's response to the presence of bTB in hounds had been negligent. It was also put forward that there is evidence from research on diseases spread by hunting hounds, which had been suppressed by the government for the last 27 years. Chris Luffingham, director of campaigns at the League Against Cruel Sports, said: 'There is a clear link between hunting hounds and the spread of disease across the countryside, which places both animal health and the rural economy at considerable risk.' The PIG cited a July 2018 report by the University of Edinburgh into the Kimblewick Hunt outbreak, pointing to infected farm animals being fed to hounds as the probable source of infection. The group called for an immediate ban on the feeding of livestock to hunting hounds, asserting that there is clear evidence that bTB infected hunting hounds have geographically spread bTB. They went on to criticise DEFRA's actions after the Kimblewick Kennel's outbreak. DEFRA banned the feeding of offal, but PIG said bTB was not confined to offal, and that DEFRA's policy was inadequate.

Other bTB infected wildlife and threats that help spread the disease

In Britain, foxes haven't been tested for bTB for over a decade. During 2018, French government scientists carried out tests on their foxes, and published evidence that foxes also carry and can transmit bTB. Wild foxes found in southern France had infected other species, and farm animals. There have been muted claims that foxes can carry bTB, as they have frequent contact with badgers and frequently interact with cattle – but this has never been taken seriously in the UK. Wildlife campaigners maintain that it goes some way to vindicating their claim that the badger cull is not based on facts and science, and that it needs to be stopped.

There has not been enough research done on this topic, and it is feared that if foxes are found to be infected with bTB, then there could be a backlash against foxes – resulting in them being wiped out. DEFRA maintain that they have conducted research, surveys, and risk assessments, and can confirm that "foxes do not constitute a wildlife reservoir of bTB infection." There appears to be a consistent denial, when it comes to the theory that foxhounds are the ones spreading bTB across farms and countryside when out exercising, "autumn hunting", or "trail hunting". Why does DEFRA seem so unconcerned about the idea that hounds could be playing a significant role in spreading bTB? Unsurprisingly, the fox hunting community have come up with all sorts of excuses. A spokesperson for the Master of Foxhounds Association said they were aware of some new cases of bTb – in cattle near areas where hunts have been – but that the hounds had a different strain of tuberculosis to the infected cattle. APHA, which traced the Kimblewick outbreak, declined to comment. The Kimblewick Hunt admitted that they 'met at Roke on December 10 but did not go to Britwell Salome or anywhere near the farm which suffered a TB outbreak.' For many people, it is ridiculous to allow hunts to take their hounds across areas where bTB is prevalent. It's become an utter farce, but unfortunately the current government – as of 2019 – are largely pro-hunting. Therefore, the plight of foxes and badgers is unlikely to move them.

Scientists appear to be of the opinion that the primary route of bTB infection is via cow-to-cow contact. So, it would come as no surprise if the movement of infected cattle onto previously uninfected premises was found to be a significant cause for the spread of bTB. Guidance was published by APHA in October 2014 on the pre-movement and post-movement testing of cattle in England, Scotland, and Wales, to control the spread of BTB. The booklet was updated in December 2018. It suggested that even pre-movement testing wouldn't necessarily safeguard the spread of infection, because tests don't always identify infected cattle. Therefore, each movement of cattle around the UK carries the risk of transmitting infection. Farmers sourcing stock from another herd are advised to request herd details, regarding the testing that has been carried out for bTB. APHA suggest that "asking for information about the disease history of an animal and the herd it comes from will help you make a decision about the level of risk and how to manage it." It has been alleged that many vendors do not provide information about their cattle's bTB status, and the demand for this from purchasers has been somewhat limited.

All cattle movements have to be reported to the British Cattle Movement Service (BCMS). The movement has to be recorded on each cow's passport before the animal leaves the holding, and within 36 hours of the animal's arrival at the new holding. It has been estimated that about 1.7 million cattle were moved within and between different risk areas in the UK during 2016. It is believed that the number of movements has been broadly similar over the past few years. The records show considerable numbers of cattle being moved from high risk areas to lower risk areas. Even if only a small number of infected cattle have been in transit, it still poses a considerable threat as a source of new infections. Surely DEFRA and the NFU are aware of this? Movement of cattle around the country can still spread bTB, even if the majority of cattle have been pre-movement and post-movement tested.

Over the years, wildlife groups have called on the government to support a nationwide vaccination programme for badgers. A growing number of wildlife groups have been trapping badgers, injecting them with the vaccine, and then releasing them back into the wild. There had been a global shortage of the vaccine, but one wildlife group – Derbyshire Wildlife Trust – managed to import the vaccine from Canada to restart vaccinating badgers again. The Trust said that more and more landowners and farmers had been contacting them wanting to join their efforts in vaccinating badgers on their land. DEFRA says it is funding major research into a cattle vaccine, but they still have some scientific obstacles to overcome and extensive field trials to set up. A cattle vaccine should be the long-term solution, but EU rules currently prevent it being tested and used in the UK. At the end of the day, bTB is a cattle problem, and shouldn't be portrayed as a badger problem.

Counting the costs of badger culling in the UK

There has been a tremendous amount of money spent on killing our protected badgers over the years. It is estimated that over £50 million of British taxpayers' money has been spent on culling 66,704 badgers since 2013. There have been some expensive studies and reports too, which have also cost millions, going back to the 1970s. Then there is compensation to farmers for well over 250,000 infected cattle that have been culled since 2008. This has cost the British taxpayer around £500 million. To think of all the badgers who have been killed in the badger culls ... it has been nothing less than a terrible tragedy. Even more so, when scientists, independent vets, and experts are saying that there is no concrete evidence that the badger culls have been successful in eradicating bTB.

A few last words ...

Dominic Dyer, chief executive of the Badger Trust, summed up the badger culls in this statement: 'This is the largest destruction of a protected species in living memory. By the end of 2018, the government will have spent over £50m of public funds killing over 67,000 badgers (since 2013), which could push the species to the verge of local extinction in areas of England, where badgers have lived since the ice age. The badger cull is a cruel, costly and ineffective policy, and its continuation is a national disgrace.'

THE BADGER TRUST   Website: www.badgertrust.org.uk

Email: staff@badgertrust.org.uk   Registered Charity No. 1111440

"The Badger Trust exists to promote and enhance the welfare, conservation and protection of badgers, their setts, and their habitats for the public benefit. We are the leading voice for badgers and represent and support around 60 local voluntary badger groups and thousands of supporters and followers. The Badger Trust provides expert advice on all badger issues and works closely with the government, police, and other conservation organisations. We use all lawful means to campaign for the improved protection of badgers and are a member of Partnership for Action Against Wildlife Crime (PAW) and Wildlife and Countryside Link."

CHAPTER NINE
Dying Oceans

"If the oceans die, we all die."

Paul Watson

Oceans are one of the planet's most precious resources

Oceans are the most extensive, enigmatic, and amazing places – assisting the greatest biodiversity on our planet. They are vast and deep, and cover more than 70 per cent of the earth's surface. On average, the water in our oceans is 2.3 miles deep. Obviously, it is much shallower in some areas, but it can be as much as 7 miles deep in other areas. There is so much we haven't explored yet, but humans are already destroying and threatening marine life by polluting the sea. We are not helping ourselves either, when we consider that the oceans produce around 50 per cent of the oxygen we breathe. On the other hand, the oceans actually absorb around 50 per cent of all man-made climate-warming carbon dioxide.

Currently, the absorption of carbon dioxide is estimated to be at around 22 million tons a day, and this is changing the ocean's chemistry. When carbon dioxide dissolves in seawater, the water becomes more acidic. In the past 200 years, the oceans have increased their acidity by 30 per cent. By the end of the century, they could be 150 per cent more acidic than they are now. The speed of change in the ocean's chemistry is far too fast for marine life to change and adapt. Already it is impacting the shells of many sea animals – dissolving said shells entirely. Scientists say that if we manage to reduce the amount of carbon dioxide being added to the atmosphere, the global system can recover its balance again. We just need to stop overloading our atmosphere with carbon dioxide, to make our planet liveable. It's a nice thought, but who knows how long that will take? Unfortunately, there are many more problems for our marine life to cope with. We have been aware of significant pollution in our oceans for decades. Marine life is dying, and we know about that too. Yet somehow in our daily lives we barely give any consideration to the dreadful harm we are doing to the whole oceanic ecosystem of our planet. Then, millions of people around the world watched the BBC's "Blue Planet II", narrated by David Attenborough, and appeared to wake up to the terrible state of our oceans. Who could deny the horror of an albatross feeding its babies pieces of plastic, having mistaken plastic for food, or the female dolphins exposing their calves to pollutants through their contaminated milk? In the words of David Attenborough:

"We are at a unique stage in our history. Never before have we had such an awareness of what we are doing to the planet and never before have we had the power to do something about it. Surely we have a responsibility to care for our Blue Planet. The future of humanity and indeed all life on earth now depends on us."

Many people seem to have now woken up to the horror we have created, and the need to acknowledge not only the problems, but to understand our individual role in what is happening out there. Every single one of us has a part to play in saving our oceans.

The reality is, we are simply using the sea as a dumping site for our trash. Consequently our oceans are suffering from toxic waste, plastic, sewage, oil spills, hazardous chemicals, radioactive waste, fertilisers, metals, pesticides, and so on. What have we been thinking for decades? Perhaps it was assumed that if we went far enough out to sea, we could get away with ditching whatever we wanted, and it wouldn't come back to haunt us. Perhaps we thought that the oceans were so colossal, so vast, that all the pollutants could be dumped into the sea and somehow become diluted and disseminated to the point they were safe. How could we have been so irresponsible and stupid? They have not disappeared or become safe. Quite the opposite, as this toxic waste has affected marine life, and consequently entered the food chain. Humans have now become contaminated from eating fish and seafood. This could cause serious problems to our health, from cancer to immune system damage. It seems there is no escape from this nightmare.

It may be helpful to understand just how important our oceans are to us as a species, and how they are a valuable natural resource that has an effect on our global weather. The ocean absorbs most of the sun's radiation, which acts as a huge heat-retaining solar panel – especially around the equator. The tropics absorb about four times more heat than the poles, because the sun's radiation hits the equator at a more direct angle in that part of the world. Scientists reckon the earth would be 20°C warmer if the oceans didn't absorb heat. Of the additional heat caused by the greenhouse effect, oceans are actually absorbing 90 per cent of that too. The ocean currents help the distribution and flow of this warm water north to the Arctic, or south to Antarctica. As the water cools, it sinks and flows southward or northward to the equator again, and warm water flows north or south to the poles to take its place. The end result is that temperatures are not extreme, which helps to moderate our climate.

Unfortunately, we have all experienced some extreme variations of weather in recent decades, and these extremes could get worse if our oceans continue to absorb the excess heat from the greenhouse effect. The oceans have become increasingly warmer over the last 50 years, and they are expected to become even warmer thanks to the current level of greenhouse gases being released into the atmosphere. In turn, warmer oceans change weather patterns, causing powerful tropical storms, and harming marine life. The entire ecosystem that animals and plants (and people too!) depend on to survive, is being altered. Plants start growing earlier, and continue to survive longer into the autumn months. Animals wake up earlier from hibernation, and there have been changes to their migration patterns. Some plant and animal species need to survive in colder regions. As those areas become warmer, said species are no longer able to exist. Our coral reefs, home to many fish and other marine creatures, are already feeling the effects of warmer sea temperatures and increased ocean acidity, caused by more carbon dioxide in the atmosphere. They are suffering from "coral bleaching", which is damaging the coral and homes of many sea creatures, and will affect the food network that many living things in the ocean rely on for survival.

Our oceans command the weather. They also help to clean the air and provide a vital source of protein in fish, to feed the human world. Our oceans allow the fisheries and other industries to support the livelihoods of up to 540 million people (8% of the world's population) either directly or indirectly. They are also home to most of life on earth, from tiny microscopic algae to the largest animal on the planet – the blue whale. Yet we are killing our oceans. We can talk about governments in every country having a responsibility, and lay the blame with big industrial companies who send their toxic waste out to sea, or with oil companies who spill toxic chemicals into the oceans. We can point the finger in so many places, and it's easy enough to do, but at the end of the day each and every one of us is responsible for the damage and pollution in our oceans across this planet. Many of us drive cars, use oil for heating, buy the products made in industrial factories, use plastic for convenience, use electricity from nuclear power stations, rely on sewage systems, use fertilisers in our gardens ... the list goes on. We take our everyday conveniences for granted, but they come at the expense of polluting our oceans and killing marine wildlife.

How do pollutants end up in our oceans?

According to the National Oceanic and Atmospheric Administration (NOAA) of the US Department of Commerce, approximately 1.4 billion pounds of trash enters our oceans every year, and this has a drastic effect on marine wildlife. Plastic is the most common item. Some of this trash ends up on our beaches, having been washed in with the tide, and originating from countries thousands of miles away. If we look at plastic, then there are many ways it can find its way into the sea. It is probably the most common item, and a very harmful one too, because it doesn't break down easily. Approximately 80 per cent of marine pollution comes from land-based activities. This all causes untold damage to the marine environment. Tiny organisms like plankton ingest the chemicals as they feed. Then these organisms are eaten by small marine animals, helping the chemicals to become more concentrated. Then larger marine animals eat the smaller marine animals, and so forth, until animals further up the food chain end up with toxic contamination levels – millions of times higher than the sea in which they live. It's very distressing to know that polar bears at the highest level of the food chain can have contamination levels 3 billion times higher than what is found in their environment. So, what does this say about the human population – who eat fish and other marine life in the oceans? Simply, it is conceivable, likely even, that humans are also contaminated by pollutants from the sea.

The most obvious way that trash ends up in our oceans, is by ships dumping it directly. It is incredible that it is legal to dump trash like paper and rags, glass, raw sewage, metal or similar refuse, as long as you are at least 12 miles from the coast. It takes 6 weeks for a newspaper to disintegrate in the sea. A cigarette filter can take between 1-50 years. A tin can and a foam plastic cup can take 50 years, disposable nappies 450 years, plastic bottles 450 years, monofilament fishing lines 600 years, and glass bottles 1,000,000 years. Think of an average size cruise ship, dumping about 30,000 gallons of raw sewage into the oceans each day. Such vessels also produce about 7 tons of garbage and solid waste each day. They are capable of producing an output of pollution emissions in one day that equals about 12,000 motor vehicles. The only trash that cannot be legally dumped in the sea is plastics. In the words of Paul Watson, founder of the Sea Shepherd Conservation Society:

"From every port and sewer in the world we dump, spew and pump toxic filth into the sea. We need to give our ocean time to repair the damage we have done. And remember, when the oceans die, we all die!"

Sewage in many parts of the world flows untreated into the oceans. 80 per cent of untreated urban sewage is discharged into the Mediterranean Sea. Even in the UK, we have areas where raw sewage is discharged into the sea on a daily basis. The effect of untreated sewage entering into the sea is in the bacteria in human waste, like E.coli, infecting the water and spreading disease. Then there are other harmful solids and chemicals in sewage, all of which can devastate areas of water that support marine wildlife. Water contaminated with sewage causes eutrophication. This is where a body of water has an overabundance of nutrients such as nitrates, phosphates, and organic matter, which is found in human waste. This is good for algae and bacteria, which take over and cause dense growth, but has negative effects on the marine ecosystem. The effects can be long-term, as the algae can block light from reaching the water. In turn, this prevents aquatic plants from photosynthesising and providing oxygen to marine creatures like fish and crabs.

Agricultural fertilisers on farms can find their way into local streams, rivers, and groundwater, and will eventually make their way to the coast and into the sea. They also cause eutrophication in estuaries, bays, and deltas, where little or no marine life can exist. Scientists have documented about 400 areas of dead zones in the world, including those in the oceans as well as those inland. But the general opinion is that the number of dead zone areas could be higher. Some of the largest and most notorious areas are the Gulf of Mexico, the Baltic Sea, and the Arabian Sea – which is described as the largest and thickest dead zone in the world.

Nuclear radiation occurs naturally, but it has many different forms – many of them man-made. Some are much more poisonous than others. Nuclear power stations, reprocessing plants, and the military, all produce nuclear waste. Nuclear radiation is transmitted in invisible rays and can be weak or strong, and very harmful. Low levels of radioactive waste have been charged into the Irish Sea, the English Channel, and the Arctic Ocean, and can enter the food chain through plankton, which are then eaten by fish. It's distressing to know that radioactive caesium (used in radiotherapy) and plutonium (produced in a nuclear reactor by neutron bombardment of uranium) have been found in seals and porpoises in the Irish Sea. In 2011, when an earthquake and tsunami hit Japan, it inflicted terrible damage to the Fukushima Daiichi nuclear plant. As a result, thousands of tonnes of radioactive water was released into the Pacific Ocean. We do not fully know what devastation this has caused in the short term, and in the future, to the marine wildlife in the surrounding sea.

Industrial waste is often directly discharged into the sea. Dumping toxic liquids directly into the water affects marine wildlife, because these toxic liquids are extremely hazardous and they can raise the temperature of the ocean – causing marine life to perish. Items like batteries contain a high number of toxic metals and chemicals like lead oxide. Mining sites often dispense a number of hazardous chemicals as waste, including lead, chromium, asbestos, arsenic, cadmium, and mercury. Mercury is extremely damaging to human health, as it can severely damage the brain and nervous system when inhaled or made contact with. So, it should come as no surprise that whales and dolphins across our oceans are dangerously contaminated by mercury and other heavy metals that have been dumped in the sea. This impacts the reproductive system of marine animals, leading to failure in breeding and ultimately to the extinction of many species. Research has shown that tests on whale and dolphin meat in Japan have disclosed very high levels of mercury – up to 5000 times the Japanese government's limit for mercury contamination. Yet the Japanese still continue to catch whales for "research", even though they are breaking international law, and sell this meat to the public. They also slaughter pods of dolphins, after they have chosen a few unblemished ones to sell to marine parks and dolphinariums, where said dolphins go on to die slowly in captivity. The meat from the slaughtered dolphins goes into frozen storage to sell for human consumption. But, with sales of whale and dolphin meat falling over the years, they now put it into pet food production. This includes the fin whale meat they import from Iceland – with these whales still being unethically caught, of course.

Oil spills are particularly damaging for marine life, because oil coats everything it comes into contact with, and can cause severe damage to the environment. This damage often lasts for decades. Spills can be caused by offshore oil rigs, pipelines, and damaged oil tankers on the sea and refineries, and waste industrial oil on land. When crude oil reaches a beach, the oil coats and attaches itself to every rock, pebble, and grain of sand. It also coats marine mammals and birds. Oil will destroy the insulating capability of mammals with fur, such as sea otters, and the water-repelling ability of a bird's feathers. If the creatures try to clean themselves, they can ingest the oil, which will poison them. If oil seeps into coastal marshes and wetlands, it will make the area unsuitable as a wildlife habitat. Out at sea, when the oil slick stops floating on the water's surface, it will start to sink down into the marine ecosystem – harming fish and shellfish.

Most of the oil spills and seepages from land are everyday occurrences. Millions of gallons enter our oceans every year, with over half coming from land drainage and waste disposal. Offshore drilling and production operations, together with spills and leaks from ships and tankers, account for about 8 per cent of the total. The remainder comes from maintenance of ships, hydrocarbon particles from onshore pollution, and natural seepage from the sea floor. But when there is a major incident – like the 1989 Exxon Valdez tanker spill in Alaska's Prince William Sound – we are looking at a disaster of immeasurable proportions.

The 1989 Exxon Valdez oil spill is considered to be the second major oil spill after the Deepwater Horizon oil spill in the Gulf of Mexico. Over 11 million gallons of crude oil were discharged into the waters of the Gulf of Alaska, killing hundreds of thousands of species. The oil tanker Exxon Valdez was carrying an estimated 54 million gallons of oil, when it struck the Bligh Reef in the Prince William Sound region of Alaska. The hull of the vessel was torn open, and over 11 million gallons of crude oil escaped into the waters. It was an ecological disaster, and contaminated over 1,300 miles of coastline. A delay in starting the clean-up efforts made the disaster more catastrophic, as the oil slick expanded to more areas within days, and was no longer containable. In order to disperse the oil, rescue teams sprayed oil dispersant chemicals in the water and on shore, thereby putting more chemicals into the sea. It was estimated that around 250,000 seabirds, 2,800 sea otters, up to 300 harbour seals, 250 bald eagles, and at least 22 orcas were killed. A huge number of herring and salmon died, along with the death and contamination of crab, rockfish, shrimp, etc. It was reported that the oil spill affected more than 26,000 jobs in the tourism industry, and over $2.4 billion in business. The impact of this man-made disaster is still being felt by marine life today, and this will go on into the future. There are still pockets of crude oil in some locations. A 2001 study found that oil contamination remained at more than half of the 91 beach sites tested in the Prince William Sound. To this day, stocks of herring have still not returned to their original number.

Similarly, the 2010 BP Deepwater Horizon offshore drilling disaster had a lasting impact on even the smallest organisms in the Gulf of Mexico. It contaminated more than 1,300 miles of coastline, coating seabirds with oil and killing marine wildlife, as well as costing the tourism and fishing industries huge financial losses. It covered an area of 68,000 square miles of ocean, and leaked over 1 billion gallons of crude oil. The oil well was located nearly a mile from the surface of the sea, in a permanently dark environment with cold temperatures. Over 1.4 million gallons of chemical dispersants were used in the clean-up operation, putting more pollutants into the ocean. Seabird losses amounted to hundreds of thousands, but many more birds may have been affected, living in the marshes along the Gulf coast. Dolphin and sea turtle deaths increased threefold in the two years after the oil spell. Fish and shrimps were affected, along with deep water corals that were found covered in oil. For years after the oil spill, there were reports of eyeless and deformed shrimp, and deformities and lesions in fish. Only time will tell if the marine ecosystem in the Gulf of Mexico can recover from the atrocity.

Ocean mining has the potential to wreak devastation on the fragile marine ecosystem, and environmentalists are always worried by the prospect of deep-sea mining, especially after the BP Deepwater Horizon oil tragedy. Ocean mining sites are generally set up for the drilling and extraction of silver, gold, zinc, copper, and cobalt. Humans have only managed to explore about 10 per cent of the ocean. If something goes wrong at depths of 2 miles or deeper, putting it right is extremely difficult compared to fixing problems at the surface. We know that deep sea mining causes damage to the lowest levels of the ocean and increases the toxicity of the area. At the entrance to some of these hydrothermal vents, are some of the planet's richest but most barely studied ecosystems. Unfortunately, the conflict between commerce and conservation is wide, and countries like China are very determined to exploit our sea floor. It is believed that there are vast quantities of certain metals in certain areas of the seabed, which has led to a revival of interest from several countries. Commercial deep sea mining has not yet occurred, because said work has been proposed to take place in unknown depths of the oceans. Very little is understood about this marine habitat. If mining was to go ahead, then the risk of irreversible environmental damage is very real.

We tend to think of the ocean as a silent, underwater world. But that couldn't be further from the truth. Noise pollution, mainly from shipping traffic, seriously disturbs marine life. Sound waves travel farther and faster under water in the oceans, than they do in the air. How fast they are transmitted depends on the ocean temperature and pressure. Marine mammals like whales and dolphins, along with fish and other marine wildlife, rely on communication by sound to find food, mate, and navigate. Hence, marine life is extremely sensitive to noise pollution. Roughly 60,000 commercial tankers and container ships are on the seas at any given time, and together they make a constant loud and noisy din under water. This can reach nearly every corner of the oceans, and weakens the sensory range of marine wildlife. The death of marine animals can happen in merely hours after exposure to extreme underwater noise. The beaching of whales has been linked to high-intensity sonar, commonly used by the US Navy.

Seismic surveys are used to produce detailed images of local geology, to discover the size and location of potential oil and gas reserves. They use a combination of high-powered air guns, water guns, and other acoustic sources. These can be fired every 10 to 12 seconds for weeks or even for months on end. These deafening seismic blasts can travel as far as 2,500 miles. Dynamite use has been stopped in marine seismic surveys, because of the danger it poses to marine life. Some organisations will argue that, contrary to the claims of some environmental groups, seismic surveying and "numerous" research projects have proved that there is no evidence that offshore seismic surveys harm marine animals or their marine ecosystems. They claim that the companies involved employ extensive precautions to minimise any disturbances to these animals, and that whale populations continue to thrive. But many environmentalists are sceptical of these claims, because of the huge amounts of profit these companies stand to gain.

Plastic – the curse across the planet

We created plastic 100 years ago, and now we cannot get rid of it. Plastic doesn't biodegrade, so therefore it doesn't go away. It can become brittle and break down into tiny pieces, but it's still there, and probably will still be wherever it was dumped in a few thousand years. At the end of 2017, 200 countries pledged to stop dumping plastic in the world's oceans. They signed a UN resolution to eliminate plastic in the sea, with the hope that it would lead to a legally binding treaty. Eight million tons of plastic are dumped into our oceans every year. If this continues by 2050, there will be more plastic in the sea than fish. The amount of plastic floating on the surface of the sea accounts for only 5 per cent of plastic trash. The other 95 per cent is submerged beneath, and it is this plastic that devastates marine wildlife and the marine ecosystem. It's an absolute tragedy. It's reported that five countries in Asia are attributed with dumping as much as 60 per cent of plastic waste in the planet's oceans. They are China, the Philippines, Indonesia, Thailand, and Vietnam. It seems that Asia is following the American trend of consuming fizzy drinks in plastic bottles, takeaway meals served in polystyrene boxes, trainers, and other items that produce plenty of throwaway trash. In these countries, they don't have adequate refuse collection. Trash can be piled high in communal dumps, where it can be swept out by the wind and washed out by the rains to end up in the sea.

Hence, we have the "Great Pacific Garbage Patch" (GPGP) which is essentially a giant whirlpool, where much of the trash discarded in the Pacific ends up. In photos it looks like a floating island of garbage. Around the GPGP, the water is cloudy with microplastics. They are everywhere. These primary microplastics are essentially microbeads, which are tiny pieces of manufactured plastic measuring from 10 micrometres to 1 millimetre in size. They can be difficult to see with the naked eye, yet they are added to toothpaste, exfoliating face scrubs, shower gels, soap, sunscreen products, and cosmetics. Normally, they are made of polythene, but they can be made of other petro-chemical plastics, such as polypropylene and polystyrene.

Microbeads may seem harmless, but 100,000 can be washed down the sink after using some products or after just one shower. They make their way to the sea, where they are digested by marine life and end up in the food chain for human consumption. The irony is that we don't need microbeads in our products, and we certainly don't need them contaminating our oceans. The UK government pledged to ban plastic microbeads in 2016, following a US ban in 2015. In 2018, the ban was introduced in the UK. With an estimated 5 trillion pieces of plastic in our oceans, something had to be done. You may be shocked to discover that the River Tame, near Manchester, has the highest microplastic pollution discovered anywhere in the world! Back in 2015, Australian scientists published a study which concluded that over 90 per cent of seabirds probably had plastic in their stomachs. These plastic fragments can absorb toxic chemicals from ocean pollution and can poison whatever organism eats them. We now have 180 species of marine wildlife which have been certified as consuming plastic. This ranges from tiny micro creatures like plankton, to huge mammals like whales. Even a third of UK caught fish have plastic inside their gut, and these include species regularly eaten by humans. Research has shown that when fish are given the choice between natural and microplastic pieces, they tend to go for the plastic. How does this affect humans who eat a seafood-rich diet during their lifetime? There has been some research done on this, involving fish and other marine animals, but we don't know very much about the long term effects for humans ingesting plastics as yet.

It has been estimated that about 100,000 marine mammals, and a million sea birds, are killed annually by eating waste and plastic, or after becoming entangled in abandoned fishing nets – which includes those nets that are plastic. There have been some alarming images of turtles eating plastic bags that fill and flap around in the sea. They mistake them for jellyfish, and like fish and dolphins, the bags cause blockages in their digestive system and breathing channels, resulting in death. Plastic six-pack rings for drink cans can also choke marine wildlife. Amongst the contents of seabirds' stomachs have been cigarette lighters, toothbrushes, and tampon cases. Scientists have discovered that pharmacy medication taken by humans but not fully processed in our bodies, has also found a way into the fish we eat. The most likely route is via raw sewage, pumped out directly into the sea.

There is no end of books, groups, and charities for support and information on how to give up plastic in your daily life. Plastic pollution across the planet is one of the major issues we need to tackle, right now, starting today. Our wildlife is suffering and dying from the scourge of plastic garbage, and each and every one of us has a duty to do something about it. We can start in our homes, getting rid of our reliance on plastic, but we also need to tackle the plastic curse in the workplace, in our schools, colleges, and universities, in our parks and recreational grounds, and anywhere else we go on this planet.

A few last words ...

Now that the human race is beginning to understand the extent of the pollution of our oceans, we must respond immediately. Our oceans are choking from debris and toxic waste. Marine wildlife is dying, and many species are on the verge of extinction. We need our governments to enforce international laws and punish perpetrators, wherever they are in the world. The blame lies with us – we must amend our mistakes before it's too late.

SEA SHEPHERD UK   Website: www.seashepherd.org.uk

Registered Charity No: 1110501

"Established in 1977, our mission is to end the destruction of habitat and slaughter of wildlife in the world's oceans in order to conserve and protect ecosystems and species."

"By safeguarding the biodiversity of our delicately balanced ocean ecosystems, Sea Shepherd UK works to endure their survival for future generations."

MARINE CONSERVATION SOCIETY Website: www.mcsuk.org

Email: info@mcsuk.org   **Registered Charity No: 1004005**

"We believe too much is being taken out and too much is being put into our seas. Our scientists, campaigners, volunteers, advocates, data experts, fundraisers, divers and researchers are all passionate about creating a sustainable future for our seas."

GREENPEACE UK   Website: www.greenpeace.org.uk

Greenpeace Environmental Trust Registered Charity No: 284934

"We defend the natural world and promote peace by investigating, exposing and confronting environmental abuse, and championing responsible solutions for our fragile environment."

CHAPTER TEN
Wildlife in Crisis

"It is time we all stood together, to be the voice of the voiceless before it's too late. Extinction means forever."

Paul Oxton

Mass extinction of animals on our planet

We are experiencing the worst disappearance of wildlife species on our planet since the loss of dinosaurs 65 million years ago. Over a period of time, extinction is normally a natural phenomenon. However, at the current rate, scientists estimate that we are losing 150-200 species of mammals, birds, insects, and plants EVERY DAY! Thanks to the human population, this rapid loss of wildlife is between 1,000 and 10,000 times higher than the natural extinction rate. We appear to have lost half the wildlife on our planet in the last 40 years. Why is this happening? Well, humans are killing animals at an unsustainable rate, for food and for pleasure. Humans are destroying animal habitats. Humans are polluting animals' environments on land and across the oceans. Humans choose lifestyles that appear to satisfy their needs, at the expense of the natural world. In order to rescue species from the brink of extinction, the first thing people need to know is all about the plight, the importance, and the value of said species.

The following animals are more examples of vulnerable to critically endangered species which have not yet been mentioned in this book. They throw some light on the harrowing circumstances being inflicted on these animals, all of which have been brought about by human activity on this planet.

King of the Arctic – Polar Bear

"Polar Bear on pack ice, Svalbard"

The plight of the polar bear was summed up in a harrowing video of a starving polar bear on the brink of death, taken by photographer Paul Nicklen and filmmakers from the conservation group Sea Legacy. They made the video when they came across the bear in late summer on Somerset Island, close to the larger Baffin Island, in the

Canadian Arctic. The video made the filmmakers cry, as they filmed the polar bear's agonising death. It dragged its back legs as it rummaged for food in a trashcan. But there was nothing to eat, and the bear collapsed to the ground. In this case, the polar bear wasn't dying because of climate change. He was probably dying from health issues. Sea Legacy was accused of using the film as "part of a very calculated public relations exercise." Nicklen said he didn't want the bear to die in vain. Climate change is causing problems for these bears, and scientists are telling us that the bears are going to become extinct. 'Bears are going to starve to death,' said Nicklen, 'this is what a starving bear looks like.'

It will not surprise you to learn that the polar bear's only predator, is man. Polar bears' staple diet is the blubber of seals. They catch the seals when a seal pops up for air through a breathing hole on the ice. The bears must follow the ice, because the seals live out at sea, and swim so fast that the bears are not likely to catch one in the water if they tried. Polar bears live in the northern hemisphere in the Arctic Circle. They are not found in Antarctica, in the southern hemisphere. This is where the penguins live, and outside of zoos polar bears will never have contact with penguins in the wild. The bears are called marine animals, because they spend many months each year at sea. They are the only marine animal with powerful limbs and feet that enable them to walk and run on land for miles. Due to their remote habitats in the Arctic wilderness, they have kept most of their natural terrain and environment due to the absence of human development. This is far more than any other surviving carnivore on the planet.

Polar bears exist across five countries – Denmark (Greenland), Norway (Svalbard), Russia, USA (Alaska), and Canada. These five countries are party to the International Agreement on the Conservation of Polar Bears and between them they authorise and cooperate on research and conservation efforts across their countries. The estimated population of polar bears in the world is between 20,000 and 26,000, and their conservation status is vulnerable. The loss of sea ice, due to climate change, is quoted as being the greatest threat to the survival of the polar bear. Of the 19 polar bear subpopulations, at least three are in decline, two are currently increasing, and another six are considered stable. This leaves eight subpopulations without reasonable data on their numbers. Due to living in remote areas, polar bears are difficult to monitor and survey, particularly in Russia and Greenland. In Arctic Russia especially, there is very little information, because of the extreme temperatures and lack of basic roads and airfields.

Despite polar bears being a vulnerable species, Canada still issues over 600 permits a year to hunt polar bears for subsistence and sport, which attracts many big game trophy hunters. It is seen as an important source of income for northern communities. Scientists have calculated that in some areas, the rate is not sustainable for polar bears. In Alaska, hunting polar bears has been banned, but some permits are issued to "indigenous subsistence hunters" living in coastal areas. Likewise, in Russia, hunting polar bears is only legal for indigenous peoples. Polar bears have been encroaching on their villages, endangering human life due to shrinking of the sea ice. By giving permits to indigenous peoples, it was thought that this would keep illegal hunting at bay. Greenland had no limits on the hunting of polar bears by indigenous people up until 2005. It then imposed a limit of 150, which also includes recreational hunting. Norway only allows killing polar bears in a defence situation.

POLAR BEARS INTERNATIONAL   *Website: www.polarbearsinternational.org*

"Our mission is to conserve polar bears and the sea ice they depend on. Through media, science and advocacy we work to inspire people to care about the Arctic, the threats to its future and the connection between this remote region and our global climate."

Most trafficked animal in the world – Pangolin

"Pangolin in the African bush, Hwange National Park, Zambia"

Considering the pangolin has gained the highest levels of protection under the Convention on International Trade in Endangered Species of Wild Fauna and Flora (CITES) in all 8 species, why is it still being trafficked in such huge numbers? It has been estimated that, since 2000, over one million pangolins have been traded illegally at international level. Pangolins are found on two continents, with 4 species in Africa and 4 species in Asia. In Africa, we have the black-bellied pangolin, the white-bellied pangolin, the giant ground pangolin, and Temminck's ground pangolin. In Asia we have the Indian pangolin, the Philippine pangolin, the Sunda pangolin, and the Chinese pangolin. These are all protected species under national and international law. Their conservation status on the IUCN Red List ranges from vulnerable to critically endangered. Their unique evolutionary history goes back over 80 million years, yet the human race is forcing pangolins into extinction, because of the demand for their meat and scales.

Pangolins are nocturnal creatures – shy, secretive and solitary. Their bodies are covered in scales, but they are mammals. In times of danger, they roll themselves into a ball, exposing their strong, sturdy scales to protect themselves. They feed exclusively on ants and termites, using their long sticky tongues to catch their prey. Little is known about them, but by the scale of the trafficking their numbers must be declining rapidly. Unfortunately, pangolins rarely survive in captivity, and most die within a short period of time. Therefore, it is difficult to care for injured pangolins, and those seized from illegal wildlife traders often need treatment and rehabilitation before they can be released back into the wild. Rescue centres are trying pioneering work to help rescued pangolins. The ideal situation is to put pangolins back into their natural habitat, and develop conservation efforts to protect them on the ground where they live.

What is so special about the meat and the scales of a pangolin? Well, the meat is considered a delicacy in China and Vietnam. Pangolin meat can be sold for $350-$600 per kilo to restaurants. In China, a pangolin's tongue, which can measure a foot long, is dried for people to carry as a lucky charm. Pangolin foetus is considered to be an aphrodisiac. However, the real worth is in the scales, because they are used in traditional Chinese medicine. In July 2017, customs officers in Malaysia seized approximately 8 tonnes of pangolin scales bound for China. The scales were estimated to have come from 16,000 pangolins. Apparently, these scales can cure anything from asthma to reproductive problems. They can even help with cancer. Experts seem to have a different opinion, and as the pangolin scales are made of the same keratin in human nails, it will come as no surprise for you to learn that they have no medicinal value. But the myths are still perpetuated, driven by greed and money. As a result, this beautiful creature has been virtually annihilated across two continents.

When the pangolin was hunted almost to extinction in China and Vietnam, the traffickers started to ship them over in large quantities from Africa. They take advantage of remote ivory trade routes to smuggle pangolins out of Central Africa. The pangolin's scales are its body armour, which can protect it from all predators except man. So, when a pangolin feels threatened, it rolls up into a ball instead of running away. All a human has to do is pick it up, put it into a container, and walk away with it. Nets and snares are usually set in the forests to catch pangolins. They are exported, dead or alive; but live pangolins will not survive for long when wrapped up in a bag or cage, being denied food and water. They can be fresh or frozen, gutted and skinned. If traffickers are caught they can escape fines and punishment by bribing the police. They are rarely sent to prison.

David Attenborough described the pangolin as 'one of the most endearing animals I have ever met.' They can certainly catch your heart, and are all the more amazing because we know so little about them and how they live. But in a country like Vietnam, with a population of 90 million, it is now extremely rare for the Vietnamese to see a pangolin in the wild – all thanks to a few rich businessmen and officials who want to eat them so they can flaunt their wealth in the faces of others. It's still hard to believe that in the twenty-first century humans are able to eat – to extinction – an animal that has been on our planet for 80 million years; one that causes no threat to humans or animals. Putting it politely – it is an utter disgrace.

SAVE VIETNAM'S WILDLIFE   **Website: www.svn.vn**

Email: info@svw.vn   **Non-Profit Organisation in Vietnam**

"In 2014, Vietnamese conservationists founded Save Vietnam's Wildlife. SVW commits to stop the extinction and champion the recovery of threatened species in Vietnam."

Ancient mariner of the high seas – Leatherback Turtle

"Female Leatherback Turtle on sandy beach on Caribbean Island after laying her eggs"

Leatherback turtles have been on this planet for 100 million years, and they are the largest sea turtle in our oceans. They feed on jellyfish and other jelly-like creatures.

Unlike other turtles, they don't have a bony shell covering their backs. Instead, their backs are covered by thick, leathery tough skin, supported by thousands of minute bone plates that make it look "leathery". Generally, their size is about 4 to 6 feet, though one leatherback turtle was recorded as being nearly 10 feet when it washed up on a beach in North Wales. Leatherbacks are the only sea turtles that can dive to depths of 4,200 feet, staying down there for up to 85 minutes, where they hunt deep sea jellyfish. This is because the turtles have the unique ability to maintain a warm body temperature in freezing cold water, and can adapt to survive in both tropic and temperate sea waters. Having the widest global distribution of all reptile species, they can be found in the waters of the Atlantic, Pacific, and Indian oceans, as well as the Mediterranean Sea. Leatherbacks can travel as far north as Canada and Norway, and as far south as New Zealand and South America.

Unless mating at sea, leatherback turtles are solitary creatures. The females come ashore at night to nest in the breeding season. They can lay as many as 80 fertilised eggs before covering the nest with sand. During the breeding season, the females can nest 4 to 7 times. The eggs take about 65 days to incubate, and the temperature inside the nest will determine the sex of the hatchlings. At 85.1 degrees Fahrenheit in the nest, there will be a mix of male and female hatchlings; a lower temperature will produce males and a higher temperature will produce females. It has been estimated that out of 1,000 hatchlings, only one will make it to adulthood. Male hatchlings that make it to the sea will spend the rest of their lives there, whereas female hatchlings will only stay in the sea until they are mature. After mating, they will return to the same beach where they were hatched, to nest and produce eggs for their own progeny.

Over the last century, leatherback turtles have seriously declined, particularly the Pacific populations. The Malaysian population has disappeared entirely. The IUCN has listed the leatherback turtle as vulnerable, but the Pacific and southwest Atlantic subpopulations have been listed as critically endangered. The overriding reason for the decline in leatherback turtles is human activity. The collecting of eggs from turtle nesting beaches for subsistence or as aphrodisiacs, particularly in Southeast Asia, is a very serious threat. Tens of thousands of eggs have been removed, and this has caused the extinction of leatherback turtles in Malaysia. More recently, large-scale egg theft and killing of adult leatherbacks on the beaches in Indonesia has caused serious decline in that area. In South America and the Indian Ocean, hunting and egg collecting still persists on a large scale, despite protective legislation.

Every year, hundreds of thousands of sea turtles are caught in shrimp trawl nets, on longline hooks, and in fishing gillnets. Known as "bycatch", this is a serious threat for leatherback turtles, who need to reach the surface of the sea to breathe. Therefore, they drown once caught in the nets. Habitat loss is a huge problem for leatherback turtles. Beaches are important for nesting, but due to the rising sea level and human activity (including coastal development, vehicle traffic, and tourism) leatherback turtle nesting areas are being disturbed or even destroyed.

On top of all this, we have the plastic pollution in our seas. Leatherback turtles live on jellyfish, and what could be more similar in shape than flimsy plastic bags filled with water? Many turtles are being killed by consuming plastic debris. They have downward facing spines in their throats, which means they cannot regurgitate any plastic they have swallowed. The plastic is then trapped in their stomachs, which prevents them from swallowing their natural food. Inevitably, they starve. It's unthinkable that this animal has been around for 100 million years, and yet humans are blatantly pushing it to the edge of extinction. A lot more has to be done to protect the future of this magnificent turtle species, which has never posed any threat to humans.

THE LEATHERBACK TRUST   **Website: www.leatherback.org**

Email: trust@leatherback.org   **Non-profit organisation**

"We are an international non-profit conservation organisation that protects leatherback turtles and other sea turtle species from extinction.

We deliver measurable results around the globe through our data-driven scientific research and community action programs."

Largest primate on the planet – Mountain Gorilla

"Mountain Gorilla in Uganda, Africa"

The mountain gorilla is a subspecies of the eastern gorilla, of which there are about 3,000-4,000 left in the wild. A recent census counted a minimum of 604 mountain gorillas (being over half of the population) living in the Virunga Mountains, which border the Democratic Republic of Congo, Rwanda and Uganda. The rest of the population was 400 mountain gorillas living in the Bwindi Impenetrable National Park in Uganda. These results now put the population of the critically endangered mountain gorilla to just over 1,000. This is good news, because the population in the Virunga Mountains has more than doubled in the last 30 years – a rare success story in conservation terms, despite severe threats from poaching, habitat degradation, and civil conflict. It shows what can be achieved when countries make collaborative efforts to support park staff and rangers, veterinary workers, community projects, and tourism. But we mustn't be complacent, as the mountain gorillas are not out of danger yet.

The mountain gorilla tends to be larger than the western lowland gorilla, which accounts for 99 per cent of all living gorillas, and is estimated to be around 360,000 in total number. Mountain gorillas have longer hair and shorter arms than their lowland cousins. The thicker and longer hair helps them to survive in their habitat, where temperatures drop below freezing. They live in forests high up in the mountains, and have been pushed further and higher up the mountains as humans have moved into their territories. They have also had to endure war in Rwanda in the early 1990s, and years of civil unrest in the Democratic Republic of Congo. More than 4 million lives were lost over 14 years during the war, resulting in refugees who poured into the park, making conservation work dangerous. Land in the park has been cleared for agriculture, even though the area is protected. Nearly 4,000 acres of gorilla forest have been cleared by illegal settlers in Africa's oldest National Park, Virunga National Park.

Veterinary care has been important, because gorillas that come into contact with humans can catch human diseases – when this happens the consequences are very serious for the gorilla. Mountain gorillas can die from the common cold. Interestingly, those gorillas who have been regularly visited by researchers and tourists tend to survive better than those gorillas that have not. Their increased wellbeing has been aided by better veterinary care of sick and injured gorillas.

The illegal charcoal production industry in Virunga National Park has eradicated gorilla habitat. Nearly 6 million people in the surrounding area rely on charcoal for cooking fuel. They have no access to gas, electricity, or other fuels. About three-quarters of the charcoal comes from illegally cutting down trees in the Virunga forests. The wood is then slow baked for days in dirt pits. Hence, the Virunga region is a significant deforestation area, having lost some 24,378 hectares of forest (94 square miles) from 2001 to 2014, and a significant amount more since. There is no poaching directed at mountain gorillas for bushmeat or pet trade, but gorillas have become a hindrance to the multi-dollar charcoal trade, which leads to them being killed. The industry has grown in more recent years and is now dominated by armed transnational organised crime gangs. Local people are reluctant to cooperate with efforts to stop the charcoal trade as they fear their lives would be in danger from revenge attacks.

Mountain gorillas play an important role in the biodiversity of the forests, as they spread large seeds, which are vital for the growth of plants and trees. But though there has been a welcome increase in the population of mountain gorillas, they are still very vulnerable. They breed very slowly, with females taking 11-12 years to mature and then only giving birth every 4 years. So, it takes time to increase the population. Park rangers have done an effective job of keeping poachers at bay, but the cost has been great. More than 180 rangers have been killed in Virunga over the last 20 years. The real threat for the future is in the removal of the forest for agricultural development, oil palm, or rubber plantations. It is believed that only about 20% of the mountain gorillas' habitat is in protected areas. The future for mountain gorillas still appears extremely fragile.

DIAN FOSSEY GORILLA FUND INTERNATIONAL

Website: www.gorillafund.org   **Non-profit organisation**

"The Dian Fossey Gorilla Fund International is dedicated to the conservation, protection and study of gorillas and their habitats in Africa. Our successful, integrated approach includes close collaborations with local governments and communities as well as partners from around the world."

Tallest animal on the planet – Giraffe

"Giraffe in Amboseli National Park, Kenya"

Some would say giraffes are going down the path of "silent extinction". Their plight is being overshadowed by the poaching of rhinos and elephants, the trafficking of pangolins, and the hunting of lions. Many people would be surprised to know that the giraffe has moved from a species of least concern, to the category of vulnerable. Even conservationists were shaken by the discovery that, in 2016, giraffes had declined by 40 per cent over the previous 30 years according to IUCN. Giraffes are seen to be common across Africa, but of the 9 discrete subspecies, 5 subspecies are declining, 3 subspecies are increasing, and 1 is considered stable. The trend overall is one of decline, but several subspecies are critically endangered. These are the West African giraffe, the Nubian giraffe in Ethopia and South Sudan, and the Thornicroft giraffe in eastern Zambia. The giraffe is already locally extinct in some African countries, including Nigeria, Senegal, Eritrea, Guinea, and Burkina Faso.

A fully grown giraffe can stand at nearly 6 metres in height, and they are renowned for having a lethal kick when they need to protect themselves or their young. They are not the gentle, kind creatures you may have grown up believing them to be, or the relatively tame looking animals you see in zoos. In the wild, they are cautious and protective of their young, and lions are their most significant predator. A giraffe can take on a single lion and kill it with its powerful hooves and legs. So, giraffes are only likely to be attacked if they are very young or already injured. Giraffes are fast runners, and difficult to catch. They have excellent sight, which allows them to react quickly and warn other species in the area of approaching danger. It is estimated that around 75% of young giraffes don't make it to adulthood, due to falling victim to predators. That is one of the highest mortality rates among animals living on the grasslands and savannas in Africa.

Giraffes are facing the same threats as other vulnerable African animals: encroachment from cities and towns into their habitat, war and civil unrest, ecological changes due to mining, climate change, habitat destruction, poaching for meat, and trophy hunters. Described as recreational killing, trophy hunting appears to be having a major contribution on the decline in giraffe numbers too. Add to this the illegal trade in giraffe marrow, which is touted as a cure for AIDS, and we should be very concerned about the future for giraffes.

The trophy hunters who make the journey to Africa, are overwhelmingly from the USA. According to the analysis of import data to the USA, Americans imported 21,402 bone carvings, 3,008 pieces of skin, and 3,744 miscellaneous hunting trophies from giraffes over the past decade. It's estimated that at least 3,700 giraffes were killed to account for such items. If the giraffe was to be labelled as endangered, this would put onerous restrictions on American hunters. In order to bring a trophy home, a hunter would have to prove that the taking of the giraffe trophy was in some way helping to sustain the species. Trophy hunters are always using the word 'conservation' to justify killing their quarry, but they never appear to produce adequate evidence or proof.

What is most disturbing, is that in a country like the USA, the sale of products made with genuine giraffe skin and bone is flourishing. They are being made into bible covers, knife handles, boots, pillows, upholstery, and trinkets. This is the ivory problem all over again! If American people understood that giraffes are in decline in the wild, they probably would be appalled by these products. In 2016, a Marist Poll found that 86% of Americans disapproved of trophy hunting. An investigator with a hidden camera filmed a seller of products made from giraffe parts explaining that giraffes were aggressive and had to be killed because they endangered lives and livelihoods of African villagers. Killing wild animals and selling their parts seems to be abound with untruths, just so humans can have some justification for their terrible actions.

GIRAFFE CONSERVATION FOUNDATION   Website: www.giraffeconservation.org

"To support the conservation of viable and existing habitat for giraffe."

"To identify key threats to giraffe in Africa and develop innovative ways to mitigate these."

"To raise awareness for and promote the value of giraffe conservation in African Range States and internationally."

Man of the forest – Orangutan

"Baby Orangutan looking into camera lens"

There are two species of orangutan, the Bornean and Sumatran. They live on the islands of Borneo and Sumatra in south-east Asia, in the tropical rainforests that are crucial to their survival. The Bornean species can be divided into three subspecies: Northwest Bornean, Northeast Bornean, and Central Bornean. The Northwest Bornean subspecies is the most threatened subspecies, having been severely affected by logging and hunting. Orangutans are the largest tree climbing mammals in the world and they travel by moving from one tree to another. The Sumatran orangutans rarely climb down to the ground, whilst the Bornean orangutans will descend more often. They are very similar in appearance, and in their behaviour. Both species have reddish fur, but the Sumatrans have longer facial hair. Sumatran orangutans appear to have closer bonds with each other than their Bornean cousins. Their diet is roughly 60 per cent fruit, which includes jackfruit, durians, rambutan, mangoes, and figs. The other 40 per cent includes tree bark, woody lianas, young leaves, insects, eggs, and small vertebrates. The large males will sometimes forage on the ground, finding water in small tree holes and fruit. Orangutan males can be solitary, seemingly preferring to live on their own most of the time.

According to the latest IUCN population figures, Sumatran orangutans in the wild are estimated at 14,600, and Bornean orangutans in the wild are estimated at 104,700. They are both on the critically endangered list, having lost more than 50% of their populations in the last 40 years. At this rate, they could become extinct in the next 50 years. Orangutans can live for up to 50 years in the wild. The females become sexually mature at around 12-16 years of age. They give birth at most once every 5 years, and the intervals between the babies can be as long as 10 years. The offspring stay close to their mothers until their teens. Due to the lengthy time taken to reach sexual maturity, and the long periods between births and single births, they are considered to have a low reproductive rate. Therefore, orangutan populations take a long time to recover from population declines.

The greatest danger to orangutans is large scale deforestation. Orangutans have lost over 80% of their habitat in the last 20 years. Forests can quickly be cleared for palm plantations, transmigration settlements, and illegal logging. First, a road is built through unspoilt forest, which then brings in the contractors, settlers, and poachers. These rich forests are not only home to orangutans, but also to endangered Sumatran tigers, elephants, and rhinoceroses. The loggers move in and commence clearing the forest of its trees. Slash and burn methods are used, which causes the peat and coal deposits in the ground to ignite; add the extra dry conditions caused by drought, and dangerous fires can take hold. This disturbs the ecosystem on a grand scale. There is no sanctuary in parks or wildlife reserves for the animals, because in the main the logging is illegal and clears the forest at industrial scale speed. Taking down mature trees reduces the amount of fruit that orangutans have to eat. In addition to this, it will trigger more hunting, as the orangutans are forced to come down from the trees because of the logging. They are much more vulnerable on the ground, and easy prey for hunters.

There is also an illegal pet trade, where baby orangutans are in great demand, despite national laws to protect them in both Malaysia and Borneo. In order to take the babies, the hunters will kill the mothers. Up to 2000 babies have been captured in Borneo and sold to Taiwan, where they are seen as exotic pets. Rich people like to keep orangutans, because it is seen as a "status symbol" of their wealth. It is illegal to keep a pet orangutan in Indonesia, but no one has ever been prosecuted for doing so. Once the orangutans reach adulthood and get too big, the owners hand them over to the authorities to deal with. These owners tend to be influential figures, like politicians, policemen, and soldiers. In Thailand, orangutans are used and abused for the tourist trade. It's pitiful and heart breaking to see them dressed in human clothes, made to box each other, or taking part in other atrocities. Humans also see them as pests, because if orangutans enter plantations or private grounds they can steal food and be disruptive. Therefore, the hunters are called to dispose of them. Hunters are happy to hunt orangutans, because they can get a high price for orangutan skulls, and the meat can be sold too. Palm oil is the biggest threat to the future of orangutans in the wild. There has been massive expansion of palm oil plantations in Borneo and Sumatra. It is traded across the world and used in 50% of all consumer goods. Half the packaged goods on supermarket shelves contain palm oil. It is also used in cosmetics, toiletries, and biofuels. Demand for palm oil in the USA has tripled in the last 5 years, causing more and more deforestation of virgin rainforest. Palm oil has become a mammoth industry, and is a curse for our planet and wildlife. More must be done by the Malaysian and Borneo governments, to protect the future of an animal that has so much in common with humans.

ORANGUTAN FOUNDATION   Website: www.orangutan.org.uk

Registered Company No: 4624177   **Registered Charity No: 1095660**

"The Orangutan Foundation is the foremost orangutan conservation organisation. We are saving Asia's critically endangered great ape by protecting their tropical forest habitat, working with local communities and promoting research and education."

Canus Rufus – Red Wolf

"Red Wolf during autumn"

In the 1970s, red wolves were declared extinct in the wild, because they were almost wiped out by hunters – and their habitat was taken over by coyotes. Fortunately, 17 red wolves were taken into captivity and bred in zoos, and in 1987 four pairs of red wolves were released in the Alligator River National Wildlife Refuge in North Carolina. Nearly three decades later, the red wolf population was as high as 130 in 2006. The red wolf's reintroduction programme was seen as one of the most innovative and successful efforts to revive a "critically endangered carnivore species". Tragically, the wolf population declined, and today only an estimate of 35 red wolves remain in the wild. There are about 200 red wolves in captivity.

The red wolf is a smaller version of the timber wolf. It is grey-black in colour, with a reddish tinge to its coat. Red wolves used to be seen across the United States, as far west as Texas, into Florida, and up into the Midwest. But now the species has lost nearly 100 per cent of its territory, and can only be found in North Carolina – in two refuges. They are primarily nocturnal creatures, living on a diet of deer and small animals, though they can eat insects and berries. Red wolves are timid and elusive, and can hunt on their own or in small packs. They tend to form pair bonds for life, with breeding pairs being the alpha male and female partners – this is similar to other wolf species and their packs.

There has been much debate about whether red wolves should be allowed to exist in the wild. Hunters and private landowners are shooting them, using the excuse that they were mistaken for coyotes. Red wolves readily breed with coyotes, and some people argue that they are no more than a coyote/timber wolf hybrid. Ironically, it was wolves that stopped the spread of coyotes. Since wolves have been hunted to excess, coyotes have been able to breed prolifically. Conservationists argue that red wolves are the most endangered mammals on the planet, and believe that the US Fish and Wildlife Service (a division of the Interior Department) have given up on the wolves. Time is running out for these animals, and if red wolves are to be saved in the wild then at the very least laws should be put in place to stop people killing them.

It is tragic that the US Fish and Wildlife Service appear to lack any incentive to help protect the red wolves. They are reputed to have stopped releasing red wolves into the designated recovery area, have stopped making inquiries into red wolf fatalities, and ended the red wolf education programme. The Service has announced its intention to shrink the red wolf recovery area by about 90%. The last of the wolves can go into zoos, providing they don't wander off federal land and get killed. It seems that the last 30 years of hard work monitoring and safeguarding efforts for the red wolves by wildlife organisations and conservationists, have been in vain. Perhaps it is a question of not being able to find resources and money from the government. Whatever the issues are, it is a sad indictment against humanity that we are letting another species fade into extinction.

RED WOLF COALITION   **Website: www.redwolves.com**

Email: redwolf@redwolves.com   **Non-Profit organisation**

"Founded in 1997, the Red Wolf Coalition (RWC) serves as the hub of private support for long-term restoration. Through a variety of programs the RWC provides the public with science-based information about the biology and ecology of this endangered predator. The RWC works with the United States Fish and Wildlife Service Red Wolf Recovery Program to stay up-to-date on red wolf restoration and management issues and to partner in the effort to maintain healthy populations of wild red wolves."

Conclusion

I wrote this book because I want to inform people about the plight of animals. I want to show you, dear reader, about the terrible situations that humans have created for the other species on our planet. For some of us, it may appear too overwhelming. We might feel useless, or powerless to try and help. But it doesn't matter how small an action you take to try to change things for the better – small positive actions can go a long way. It doesn't have to involve money. By making informed decisions, like buying less clothes, recycling household goods, and not buying items in single plastic form, you could actually save money. If every one of us did something to help reduce their carbon print, the planet would be a much better place for wildlife and for humans.

We need to preserve a healthy ecosystem. Every animal, bird, insect, and plant species has a particular role to play, and they are all connected in different, sometimes subtle, ways. Even humans are directly dependent on other species. Take bees for example. Bees are vital for the pollination of certain crops. If bees are reduced in numbers, which scientists are already telling us they are, then the growth of those crops would diminish. As a result, we (along with other species) could go hungry. Therefore, it is vital to help conserve the bees and protect their habitat.

Extinction of wildlife species will ultimately have a catastrophic impact on humans. What we are doing to animals now, is ultimately what we will end up doing to ourselves. We are intertwined with animals on this planet, and their future is our future. In the last 100 years, humans have been hell-bent on taking more and more additional land and resources for their own needs, and pushing wildlife to extinction. Most of these animals have been living on our planet for tens of millions of years. Human beings, as we know them today, evolved 200,00 years ago. Civilisation has been around for approximately 6,000 years. Industrialisation, which has had such a devastating impact on the environment, only came to prominence in the nineteenth century. Look what we have done to our planet in such an incredibly short space of time.

We cannot go on like this. Sitting back and doing nothing is not an option. Our governments have been amiss in ignoring the problems, and now we need to let them know that we will not put up with their incompetence. Humans have got to stop destroying the natural world and exterminating wildlife. Forget how much wealth you have. The way we're destroying the planet, your assets and money will not count for very much in the future. We have to find a way to co-exist with living animals, birds, insects, and plants, all of which make up a balanced ecosystem, where all things have their rightful place.

Sadly, the future of wildlife on this planet depends on the constraints that humans put on their rights and activity. As we've proved thus far, as a species we are not conditioned to accept such restraints – and our planet is suffering the consequences. We must act now, before it is too late.

Bibliography/References

William M Adams, *Against Extinction*, Earthscan, 2004

Animal & Plant Agency, *Bovine tuberculosis: Infection status in cattle in England*, DEFRA, 2014

Animal Welfare Act 2006, legislation.gov.uk

Lawrence Anthony with Graham Spence, *The Elephant Whisperer*, Pan Books, 2010

Lawrence Anthony with Graham Spence, *The Last Rhinos*, Sidgwick & Jackson, 2012

David Attenborough, *The Life of Mammals*, BBC Books, 2002

Patrick Barkham, *Badgerlands*, Granta, 2014

Rupert Barrington and Michael Gunton, *Life Story*, BBC Books, 2014

Biologist, *Badgers and Bovine TB*, Volume 59 No 5

BMJ Journals *Are Hunting Dogs Spreading Bovine TB*, Volume 180 Issue 24

BMJ Journals *'Plausible' Risk Posed by Bovine TB in Hounds*, Volume 183 Issue 7

BMJ Journals *Spreading of Bovine TB by Hunting Hounds*, Volume 183 Issue 10

BMJ Journals *Mycobacterium bovis tuberculosis in Hunting Hounds*, Volume 183 Issue 12

Nigel Bonner, *Whales of the World*, Blandford Press, 1989

Born Free Foundation, *Animal Ark or Sinking Ship? An Evaluation of Conservation by UK Zoos*, 2007

Bovine TB Eradication Programme for England, DEFRA, 2011

Bovine TB Strategy Review, DEFRA, 2018

Bovine Tuberculosis in Cattle and Badgers, 1997 Krebs Report

Bovine Tuberculosis (TB) in Domestic Pets, Public Health England & Animal & Plant Health Agency, 2017

Lord Burns, *Report of Committee of Inquiry into Hunting With Dogs in England & Wales*, gov.uk, 2000

Robert Churchward, *A Master of Hounds Speaks*, Revised Edition 1980s, League Against Cruel Sports

Council of Hunting Associations Code Of Practice, *Hunt Kennels*, Updated 2015

Adam Cruise, *The Effects of Trophy Hunting on Five of Africa's Iconic Wild Animal Populations in Six Countries – Analysis*, Conservation Action Trust, 2016

Marcus Daley, *Big Game Hunting and Adventure*, MacMillan & Co, 1937

Documentary Film, *A Whale of a Tale*, Megumi Sasaki, 2017

Documentary Film, *Blackfish*, directed by Gabriela Cowperthwaite, CNN Films, 2013

Documentary Feature Film, *Blood Lions*, presented by Regulus Vision & Wildlands, 2015

Documentary Film. *The Cove*, directed by Louie Psihoyos, 2009

Documentary Film, *The Secret World of Badger Baiters*, BBC, 2018

Documentary Film, *Trophy*, presented by Shaul Schwarz & Christina Clusiau, 2017

Martin Dorey, *No. More. Plastic.*, Ebury Press, 2018

Dominic Dyer, *Badgered To Death*, Canbury Press, 2016

Economists At Large, *The Lion's Share? On the Economic Benefits of Trophy Hunting*, 2017, Report Prepared for Humane Society International

EDULINK, *New Alliances for Tourism, Conservation & Development in Eastern and Southern Africa*, Eburon 2011

Vanda Felbab-Brown, *The Extinction Market: Wildlife Trafficking and How to Counter It*, Oxford University Press, 2017

Rebecca Giesler & Elena Ares, *Badger Culling in England Briefing Paper*, House of Commons Library, 2018

Gemma Glanville & Chris Draper, *The Application and Enforcement of the Zoo Licensing Act 1981*, Born Free Foundation, 2013